EDVARD GRIEG

SONATE Nr. 3

c-Moll / C minor
für Violine und Klavier / for Violin and Piano
Opus 45

Ausgabe nach der Edvard-Grieg-Gesamtausgabe (Band 8)
herausgegeben vom Edvard-Grieg-Komitee, Oslo

Edition in accordance with Edvard Grieg: Complete Works (volume 8)
edited by the Edvard Grieg Committee, Oslo

Herausgegeben von / Edited by

Finn Benestad

C. F. PETERS

Ein Unternehmen der EDITION PETERS GROUP
FRANKFURT/M. · LEIPZIG · LONDON · NEW YORK

Edvard Grieg

Sonate c-Moll für Violine und Klavier / Sonata in C minor for Violin and Piano

Beginn des 1. Satzes / Opening of the 1st movement

Autograph (Quelle A) · Bergen Offentlige Bibliotek, Grieg-Samlingen
Abdruck mit freundlicher Genehmigung / Reproduced with kind permission

« Quant à la troisième sonate de violon (op. 45 en ut mineur), elle est à ranger parmi les œuvres les plus géniales
qu'on ait écrites. [...] Du commencement à la fin, c'est merveilleux d'inspiration, de science, d'indépendance. »

(Ernest Closson: Edvard Grieg et la musique scandinave, Paris 1892)

„Was die dritte Violinsonate (op. 45 in c-Moll) angeht, so muss man sie den
genialsten Werken zuordnen, die je geschrieben wurden. [...] Von Anfang bis Ende
ist sie ein Wunderwerk an Inspiration, Kunstfertigkeit und Eigenständigkeit."

"Regarding the third violin sonata (op. 45 in C minor), it must be classed as
belonging to the most brilliant works ever written. [...] From beginning to end it
is a marvel of inspiration, intelligence and independence."

Vorwort

Die drei Sonaten für Violine und Klavier spielen nicht nur in Edvard Griegs eigenem Schaffen eine wichtige Rolle, sondern sind Meilensteine in der Entwicklung der norwegischen Musik in der zweiten Hälfte des 19. Jahrhunderts. In den ersten beiden Sonaten – F-Dur op. 8 (1865) und G-Dur op. 13 (1867) – verstand Grieg es auf glückliche Weise, melodische und rhythmische Merkmale der norwegischen Volksmusik einzuführen. Diese Idee ergab sich nicht etwa aus einer Laune heraus, sondern war der Versuch, aufzuzeigen, wie das musikalische Nationalkolorit alle Formen von Musik wirkungsvoll zu bereichern vermag. Griegs Augenmerk war jedoch oft weniger auf die nationalen Aspekte gerichtet als vielmehr auf ein Streben nach Universalität in seiner Musik. In einem Brief vom 25. April 1881 an seinen Biographen Aimar Grønvold verdeutlichte Grieg: „Ich leugne nicht die übertrieben norwegische Leidenschaft meiner Jugend, aber in meinem Bemühen als moderner Künstler strebe ich nach dem Universellen – oder genauer, nach dem Individuellen. Ist das Ergebnis national, dann deswegen, weil das Individuum national ist."[1] Diese Sicht trat schließlich in seiner dritten Violinsonate c-Moll op. 45 (1887) zutage, in der er spezifische Bezüge zur nationalen Musik weitgehend vermied.

Grieg schätzte seine drei Violinsonaten sehr und brachte sie mit zahlreichen bedeutenden Interpreten im In- und Ausland wiederholt selbst zur Aufführung. Zusammen mit der tschechischen Geigerin Wilhelmina Neruda (Madame Hallé) gab er zum Beispiel am 9. Januar 1900 in Kopenhagen ein Konzert, bei dem alle drei Sonaten gespielt wurden. Wenige Tage später, in einem Brief vom 16. Januar an den norwegischen Dichter Bjørnstjerne Bjørnson (Literaturnobelpreis 1903), äußerte Grieg, die drei Violinsonaten gehörten zu seinen besten Kompositionen; jede stelle einen wichtigen Abschnitt in seiner Entwicklung dar: „die erste naiv, reich an Vorbildern; die zweite national; und die dritte mit einem weiteren Horizont."[2]

Die drei Violinsonaten sind in Band 8 (1979) der *Edvard-Grieg-Gesamtausgabe* (GGA) enthalten, die in den Jahren 1978 bis 1995 bei C. F. Peters erschien.

*

Während Grieg seine ersten beiden Violinsonaten in dem kurzen Zeitabstand von nur zwei Jahren vollendete, liegen zwischen der zweiten und der dritten Sonate zwanzig Jahre – zwei Dekaden, in denen Grieg sein schöpferisches Potenzial vielfach unter Beweis stellte. Neben dem großartigen Klavierkonzert a-Moll op. 16 (1868) komponierte er zahlreiche Lieder und Klavierstücke sowie die Bühnenmusiken zu Bjørnstjerne Bjørnsons Drama *Sigurd Jorsalfar* op. 22 (1872) und zu Henrik Ibsens *Peer Gynt* op. 23 (1874/75). Mit dem Streichquartett g-Moll op. 27 (1878) und der Violoncellosonate op. 36 (1883), seinem älteren Bruder John gewidmet, erreichte Grieg auf dem Gebiet der Kammermusik einen Höhepunkt der künstlerischen Verwirklichung.

1884 wurde sich Grieg der Notwendigkeit eines dauerhaften Wohnsitzes bewusst und veranlasste den Baubeginn der Villa „Troldhaugen", etwa acht Kilometer südlich von Bergen gelegen; der Einzug im Frühjahr 1885 schien ihm dann jene seelische Stärke und Daseinsfreude zu verleihen, deren er für die Schaffung neuer, bedeutsamer Werke bedurfte.

Die Violinsonate c-Moll op. 45 wird erstmals in Griegs Brief vom 25. Juli 1886 an Dr. Max Abraham, Verlagsleiter von C. F. Peters in Leipzig, erwähnt: „Ich schreibe an einem Kammermusikwerk. Die Götter mögen aber wissen, wann es fertig wird, denn ich leide die unglaublichsten Störungen durch ausländischen Sommergästen, so dass ich der Verzweiflung nahe bin."[3]

Einem Brief vom 1. November des gleichen Jahres ist zu entnehmen, dass es durchaus auch angenehme Besucher gab, etwa eine junge Geigenvirtuosin aus Italien. Entzückt berichtete Grieg von deren erst wenige Tage zurückliegendem Besuch auf Troldhaugen, „wo sie nicht nur die Violine spielte sondern auch Champagner trank! Und Beides that sie ganz wundervoll! [...] Diese Fée ist aber auch ein allerliebstes Wesen und wenn ich wieder Etwas für die Violine verbreche, ist sie die Schuld daran."

Zweifellos wirkte die 20-jährige Teresina Tua höchst inspirierend auf Grieg, sodass er am 21. Januar 1887 seinem Freund John Paulsen in Bergen vermelden konnte: „Ich habe gerade eine Violinsonate geschrieben, die ich nun, bevor ich sie hören kann, bis zum Herbst in der Schublade belassen muß. Im Herbst dann fahre ich weg."[4]

Der Bitte seines Verlegers, ihm das Manuskript der neuen Sonate zu senden, kam Grieg zunächst nicht nach, weil er das Werk vor der Drucklegung erst hören wollte. Ein entsprechender Brief an Abraham ist zwar nicht überliefert, doch ist Griegs ablehnende Antwort aus einem Brief vom 13. Juni 1887 zu ersehen, in dem Abraham klagte: „Durch die Mittheilung, daß Sie meinen Herzenswunsch, die Welt mit Ihrem 2. Klavier Koncert bekannt zu machen, noch nicht erfüllen können u. Ihre Violinkomposition erst hören müssen, ehe Sie mir dieselbe zum Druck geben, haben Sie mir 2 Herzenswunden beigebracht [...]".

Auf die Hörprobe musste Grieg allerdings nicht bis zum Herbst warten, noch während des Sommers spielte er das neue Werk gemeinsam mit einem Geiger aus Bergen. Der Höreindruck bei dieser ersten Ausführung, die auf Troldhaugen in Anwesenheit von Griegs Freund Frants Beyer stattfand, veranlasste Grieg zu einigen kompositorischen Änderungen, deren Umsetzung er für die Zeit eines Besuches in Leipzig ins Auge fasste. Über seine Pläne ließ er Abraham in einem Brief vom 15. August 1887 wissen: „Wir gedenken, Mitte September von hier zu fahren und wenn Alles nach Wunsch geht, hoffe ich auf ein frohes Wiedersehen in Leipzig Ende October. Ich werde mir dann erlauben, Ihnen meine neue Violinsonate mitzubringen, welche ich mit dem Namen Edition Peters ‚zieren' möchte, wenn ich sie vorher mit einem tüchtigen Geiger durchstudirt habe. Die Frage ist nur diese: Ist es Ihnen angenehm, gerade eine Geigensonate von mir zu drucken, da Sie schon eine besitzen?"

Der Verleger äußerte dann am 27. August unmissverständlich: „Ich erwidere darauf: Aller guten Dinge sind 3. Gerade Ihre beiden ersten Violinsonaten sind mir, neben dem Konzert [op. 16], die liebsten Ihrer Kompositionen, ich [...] freue mich nun nicht wenig auf die dritte."

Wie vorgesehen, verließ Grieg Troldhaugen Mitte September 1887. Nach einem vierwöchigen Kuraufenthalt in Karlsbad (Karlovy Vary) trafen er und seine Frau Nina am 20. Oktober in Leipzig ein, die Ankunft ist durch einen entsprechenden

Vermerk im *Haushaltsbuch* 1887 belegt[5]. Abgesehen von einem Abstecher nach Berlin (27.–31. Dezember) blieben die Griegs rund sechs Monate in Leipzig. Da Komponist und Verleger nun in derselben Stadt lebten, gibt es aus diesem Zeitraum keine Briefe; es ist aber anzunehmen, dass Grieg bald nach seinem Eintreffen in Leipzig das Manuskript der Sonate an Abraham gab und mit diesem ersten Schritt die Drucklegung einleitete.

Am 31. Oktober berichtete Grieg in einem Brief an Frants Beyer, er und seine Frau hätten wenige Tage zuvor einen talentierten Landsmann zu Gast gehabt: Johan Halvorsen, zu dieser Zeit Student des russischen Violinvirtuosen und Lehrers am Leipziger Konservatorium Adolph Brodsky. Halvorsen, so heißt es in Griegs Brief, „machte einen aufrichtigen und zuverlässigen Eindruck. [...] Ich hoffe, ihn besser kennenlernen zu können, was jedoch nicht so einfach ist, da wir nicht an den gleichen Orten verkehren. Ich ertrage die Nachtcafés von Leipzig nicht [...]."[6] Dem Haushaltsbuch ist zu entnehmen, dass auch am 19. November ein Treffen mit Halvorsen stattfand („Abend mit Halvorsen – 17 Mark"), wahrscheinlich nach einer intensiven Probe, auf die sich Grieg in seinem Brief vom 22. November an Beyer bezieht: „Neulich abends war er hier und spielte mit mir die Sonate, und er tat es mit solcher Herzlichkeit und wahrer Kunstfertigkeit, dass ich stolz darauf bin, dass er mein Landsmann ist."[7] Halvorsen stellte diese Begebenheit in einer Jahrzehnte später verfassten, unveröffentlichten Sammlung autobiographischen Materials (aufbewahrt in der Nationalbibliothek Oslo, früher Universitätsbibliothek Oslo) nur geringfügig anders dar. Eigentlich sei Brodsky für die Uraufführung vorgesehen gewesen, doch, so Halvorsen weiter, „ich war der erste, der die Sonate spielte. Grieg suchte mich eines Tages in meinem Zimmer auf, das Manuskript in der Hand, und wollte wissen, wie die Geigenstimme klinge. Ich glaube, daß ich ihm damals helfen konnte. Wir spielten die Sonate einige Male, und ich war von dem Werk sehr fasziniert."[8] Laut Halvorsen machte in dieser Zeit nicht nur Grieg die Bekanntschaft mit Brodsky, sondern auch der Komponist Christian Sinding.

Der letzte Eintrag bezüglich Johan Halvorsen im Haushaltsbuch datiert vom 20. Dezember 1887: „Halvorsen – 50 Mark", damals ein stattlicher Betrag und vermutlich als Honorar für die geleistete Unterstützung gedacht. Grieg schätzte Halvorsens Mitwirkung offenkundig, bezieht sich jedoch nicht ausdrücklich darauf.

Im bereits erwähnten Brief vom 22. November 1887 an Beyer schreibt der Komponist über seine Begegnung mit Adolph Brodsky: „Ich komme gerade von Professor Brodsky, Halvorsens Lehrer. Mit ihm habe ich die neue Violinsonate gespielt, von der Du im Sommer einen so schlechten Eindruck erhieltest. Damals war ich ebenso enttäuscht wie Du, doch heute abend habe ich (nachdem ich das weniger Gelungene veränderte) eine Freude erlebt, die einem Künstler nicht oft zuteil wird. Er spielte *absolut meisterhaft* und war von meinem Werk außerordentlich begeistert. Ich schwöre Dir, ich habe sie nicht wiedererkannt. Das war es wohl, was ich mir vorgestellt hatte, doch ich hatte nicht geglaubt, daß ich das, was ich meinte, auch ausdrücken konnte."[9]

Brodsky beabsichtigte, die Sonate in das Programm eines geplanten Kammermusik-Konzertes in Leipzig aufzunehmen und bat den Komponisten inständig um dessen Mitwirkung. Dieser ließ sich darauf ein und kommentierte in einem Brief vom 3. Dezember 1887 an seinen dänischen Kollegen Nils Ravnkilde in Rom: „Ich bin ein Narr, denn ich habe die nötige Kraft nicht, aber er flehte mich an, und er spielt so unwiderstehlich großartig, daß ich gänzlich gefangengenommen bin."[10]

Die c-Moll-Sonate wurde am 10. Dezember 1887 im Neuen Gewandhaus zu Leipzig uraufgeführt und war ein augenblicklicher Erfolg. Die Rezensionen würdigten Brodsky wie Grieg für eine von Herzlichkeit und Leidenschaft geprägte Darbietung. Am 11. Dezember schrieb Grieg dazu an Beyer: „Du kannst Dir nicht vorstellen, wie er spielte! Nach jedem Satz stürmischer Beifall und nach dem Finale mußten wir mehrmals auf die Bühne [...]."[11]

Einzig Eduard Bernsdorf – führender Rezensent der einflussreichen Leipziger *Signale für die musikalische Welt* und zeitlebens ein Kritiker der Hauptwerke Griegs – versuchte erneut sein Möglichstes, um den Komponisten zu desavouieren, dessen Mangel an Talent sich unzweifelhaft in der vor Geschmacklosigkeit und musikalischem Schwindel strotzenden Sonate offenbare!

Einige Wochen später, anlässlich eines Abendessens im Hause Brodsky, erklang das Werk ein weiteres Mal: „Ich komme gerade von den Brodskys, wo wir mit Tschaikowsky dinierten, er ist hier mit dem *großartig genialen* jungen russischen Pianisten [Wassily] Sapelnikov. Sinding und Halvorsen waren ebenfalls anwesend, die ganze Zeit über musizierten wir. Zunächst spielte ich auf Tschaikowskys Wunsch zusammen mit Brodsky meine neue Sonate, dann wurde Sindings Quintett mit Sapelnikov dargeboten und schließlich auch mein *Streichquartett*. Diese Kerle können wirklich spielen! Herrgott, wie das klang!"[12]

Widmungsträger der Sonate ist der deutsche Maler Franz von Lenbach; die Erstausgabe erschien Ende November 1887 bei C. F. Peters in Leipzig.[13] Über den sofort einsetzenden Erfolg berichtete Grieg am 24. März 1888 seinem Freund Beyer: „Stell Dir vor, die neue Violinsonate, die erst kürzlich erschienen ist, wurde bereits in 1500 Exemplaren verkauft. Dr. Abraham meint, dies sei einmalig, nicht einmal Brahms hat das geschafft."[14]

Etwa zeitgleich wie César Francks A-Dur-Sonate und drei Jahre vor Brahms' d-Moll-Sonate entstanden, fand Griegs dritte Violinsonate rasche Aufnahme in ganz Europa; fast jährlich war ein Nachdruck notwendig, die *Auflagebücher* des Verlages zeigen, dass im Verlauf von 19 Jahren bis 1906 nicht weniger als 29.000 Exemplare verkauft wurden![15]

Während die beiden vorausgegangenen Sonaten nicht zuletzt durch die Bezüge zum typisch Norwegischen Aufsehen erregten und das internationale Publikum aufhorchen ließen, erlangte Griegs c-Moll-Sonate – „mit einem weiteren Horizont" – allein kraft der ihr innewohnenden musikalischen Qualitäten Anerkennung. In seinem Buch *Edvard Grieg et la musique scandinave* (1892, S. 40) formulierte der belgische Musikwissenschaftler Ernest Closson eine, wie es scheint, geradezu repräsentative Einschätzung: „Was die dritte Violinsonate (op. 45 in c-Moll) angeht, so muss man sie den genialsten Werken zuordnen, die je geschrieben wurden. [...] Von Anfang bis Ende ist sie ein Wunderwerk an Inspiration, Kunstfertigkeit und Eigenständigkeit."

Das einleitende *Allegro molto ed appassionato* ist vielleicht Griegs bestgelungene Umsetzung der Sonatenhauptsatzform. Der Satz ist gekennzeichnet durch kraftvoll-ausdrucksstarke Intensität, die in den ergreifenden ersten Takten des Hauptthemas deutlich hervortritt; ruhige Überleitungen zwischen den Themengruppen sowie eine kühne und zugleich disziplinierte harmonische Gestalt sind hervorstechende Merkmale. Der erste Abschnitt des Es-Dur-Seitenthemas (T. 59) wird nach Grieg'scher Manier in Ges-Dur beantwortet (T. 79). Die Durchführung des Satzes ist nahezu einzigartig in Griegs Schaffen: Sie beginnt ätherisch-lyrisch im *ppp* in B-Dur (T. 145) und bringt das zweitaktige Kopfmotiv des Hauptthemas (vgl. T. 1–2) in einer überraschenden rhythmischen Augmentation, ergänzt durch eine chromatisch absteigende Basslinie im Klavier. Nach intensivem Crescendo wird der Basston *E* erreicht (T. 160), der die wörtliche Wiederholung des Abschnitts, ebenfalls im *ppp*, nun aber in A-Dur, vorbereitet (T. 163). Wiederum augmentiert, jedoch verkürzt erscheint das Motiv später im Forte (T. 246), hier *appassionato* überschrieben und von der Violine mit Doppelgriffen in der Grundtonart ausgeführt. Dieser Abschnitt leitet über zur Reprise (ab T. 262). Mit dem dritten Auftreten des Motivs in augmentierter Gestalt, diesmal unvermittelt in As-Dur (T. 400), scheint sich eine zweite Durchführung anzuschließen, was aber nicht der Fall ist. Nach 29 Takten beginnt im Pianissimo eine *presto*-Coda, auch sie basiert auf dem Zweitakt-Motiv. Mit ihr findet der Satz einen brillanten Fortissimo-Abschluss, der durch kadenzierende, scharf akzentuierte Akkorde mit Modalfärbung gekennzeichnet ist.[16]

Der in ABA'-Form angelegte zweite Satz, *Allegretto espressivo alla Romanza* (E-Dur), enthält einen der inspiriertesten musikalischen Gedanken Griegs. Das im Klavier vorgestellte und später von der Violine übernommene A-Thema zeichnet sich aus durch das besonders reizvolle Zusammenwirken von lyrischer Melodie und subtiler Harmonisierung. Der kontrastierende B-Teil, *Allegro molto* (e-Moll), basiert auf tanzartigen Viertaktphrasen, die dem *Halling*, einem norwegischen Volkstanz, verwandt sind. Fesselnde Harmonik bietet die Episode am Ende des B-Teils, in der Akkord-rückungen eine ungewöhnlich dichte und bravourös entworfene Modulation nachzeichnen (T. 189–217): beginnend in e-Moll, ge-folgt von schillernden Akkorden über einer chromatischen Bass-linie, fortgeführt über E-Dur und Es-Dur; danach setzt der A'-Teil in E-Dur ein. Selbst innerhalb der sehr facettenreichen Harmonik bei Grieg nimmt dieser Abschnitt eine Sonderstellung ein.

Die ätherische Stimmung am Ende des zweiten Satzes wird mit Beginn des dritten Satzes – *Allegro animato* (c-Moll) – durch dessen rhythmisch markantes Hauptthema in der Violine und die begleitenden Akkordbrechungen (leere Quinten) im Klavier gleichsam hinweggefegt. Es folgt ein lyrisches Seitenthema in As-Dur, dessen synkopierter Klavierpart dem musikalischen Ver-lauf einen stetig vorwärtsdrängenden Impuls verleiht. Thematisch liegt ein fest umrissenes Motiv zugrunde, das alsbald die Form einer weit ausgesponnenen, mit zunehmender Dramatik höher und höher steigenden Melodie annimmt.

Der Exposition folgt nicht, wie eigentlich erwartet, eine längere Durchführung, sondern überraschenderweise eine Überleitung mit nur wenigen Takten, die geradewegs zur Reprise führt. Somit liegt eine Form vor, die in keinem anderen Finalsatz von Grieg anzutreffen ist: ein Sonatensatz ohne Durchführung, oder, anders interpretiert, eine zweiteilige Form AB-AB' mit Coda. Der Verzicht auf eine eigenständige Durchführung ist sicher mit der feinsinnigen, vielfach schon durchführungsartig angelegten Exposition zu erklären. Die Reprise bringt sodann das B-Thema – *Cantabile ed espressivo* – in C-Dur, begleitet von harfenähnlich per-lenden Akkorden im Klavier. Eine ungestüme *prestissimo*-Coda, in der das düstere c-Moll des Hauptthemas in strahlendes Dur versetzt wird, bringt das Werk zu einem fulminanten Abschluss.

Die Violinsonate c-Moll nimmt seit mehr als einem Jahrhundert im Repertoire zahlreicher führender Geiger einen prominenten Platz ein und stellt Edvard Griegs Fähigkeit, Kammermusik „mit weiterem Horizont" zu komponieren, eindrucksvoll unter Beweis. Im Vergleich zu den beiden früheren Sonaten zeigt sie eine tiefergehende Konzentration, gepaart mit einer glücklichen Synthese aus lyrischer Expressivität und dunkel-gefärbtem, dramatischem Pathos. Sie ist romantische Kammermusik von höchstem Rang.

Kristiansand, November 2011

Prof. Dr. Finn Benestad
Herausgeber von Band 8 der Edvard-Grieg-Gesamtausgabe
(*Übersetzung: Sabine Richter*)

[1] Finn Benestad und Dag Schjelderup-Ebbe: *Edvard Grieg. Mensch und Künstler* (aus dem Norwegischen von Tove und Holm Fleischer), Leipzig 1993, S. 259 (dort mit abweichendem Wortlaut).

[2] Ebenda, S. 73 f.

[3] Griegs Briefwechsel mit Dr. Max Abraham, Verlagsleiter von C. F. Peters, und dessen Nachfolger, Dr. Henri Hinrichsen, liegt gedruckt vor: *Edvard Grieg. Briefwechsel mit dem Musikverlag C. F. Peters 1863–1907*, hrsg. von Finn Benestad und Hella Brock, Frankfurt/M. 1997, hier S. 139.

[4] Benestad und Schjelderup-Ebbe (wie Anm. 1), S. 218.

[5] In seinen *Haushaltsbüchern* (Öffentliche Bibliothek Bergen) führte Grieg, besonders bei Auslandsaufenthalten, sorgfältig Buch über seine Aus-gaben für Briefmarken, Papier, Droschken- und Zugfahrten, Backwerk, Mahlzeiten, Theater- und Opernbillets und andere Vergnügungen.

[6] 230 Briefe Griegs an Frants Beyer sind in Originalsprache (Norwegisch) erschienen in *Edvard Grieg. Brev til Frants Beyer 1872–1907*, hrsg. von Finn Benestad und Bjarne Kortsen, Oslo 1993. Zitierter Brief S. 108.

[7] 50 Grieg-Briefe an Beyer sind enthalten in *Edvard Grieg. Letters to Colleagues and Friends* (rund 500 Briefe in englischer Übersetzung von William H. Halverson), ausgewählt und hrsg. von Finn Benestad, Columbus, Ohio 2000. Zitierter Brief S. 48.

[8] Halvorsens Sammlung trägt den Titel „*Hvad jeg husker fra mit Liv (Til mine Barn)*" [Erinnerungen aus meinem Leben (Für meine Kinder)]. Zitiert nach Benestad und Schjelderup-Ebbe (wie Anm. 1), S. 218.

[9] Ebenda, S. 218 f.

[10] *Edvard Grieg. Brev i utvalg* [Ausgewählte Briefe] *1862–1907*, Bd. II, hrsg. von Finn Benestad, Oslo 1998. Zitierter Brief (norw.) S. 226.

[11] Benestad und Schjelderup-Ebbe (wie Anm. 1), S. 219.

[12] Brief vom 29. Januar 1888 an Beyer in *Grieg: Letters to Colleagues and Friends* (wie Anm. 7), S. 51. Das Verhältnis zwischen Grieg und Brodsky entwickelte sich bald zu einer lebenslangen, innigen Freundschaft. Zu Griegs Beisetzung 1907 in Bergen reiste Brodsky aus Manchester an, um seinem Freund die letzte Ehre zu erweisen und in einem von Halvorsen eigens für diesen Anlass zusammengestellten Orchester mitzuspielen.

[13] Vgl. *Edvard Grieg, Thematisch-Bibliographisches Werkverzeichnis*, hrsg. von Dan Fog †, Kirsti Grinde und Øyvind Norheim, Frankfurt/M. 2008, S. 208. Interessantes Material dokumentiert auch die Dissertation (1994) von Rolf Christian Erdahl: *Edvard Grieg's sonatas for stringed instrument and piano: Performance indications of the primary source materials* (Ann Arbor, Michigan 2001). Eine umfassende Untersuchung zu Griegs Kammer-musik liegt vor mit Benestad und Dag Schjelderup-Ebbe: *Edvard Grieg. Chamber Music: Nationalism – Universality – Individuality*, Oslo 1993.

[14] Benestad und Schjelderup-Ebbe (wie Anm. 1), S. 219.

[15] Freundliche Information von Klaus Burmeister (Dresden), früher Chef-lektor bei C. F. Peters, Leipzig.

[16] Einige Musikwissenschaftler betrachten den As-Dur-Teil (T. 400) als Beginn der Coda, so etwa Patrick Dinslage in seinem fundierten Artikel: „Zu Edvard Griegs dritter Violinsonate opus 45 in c-moll. Anmerkungen zu Harmonik und Form", in: *Studia Musicologica Norvegica*, Nr. 25, 1999, S. 108–123, hier S. 113.

Preface

The three sonatas for violin and piano, which play an important role in Edvard Grieg's oeuvre, signify milestones in the development of Norwegian music during the latter part of the nineteenth century. In the first two sonatas, Op. 8 in F major (1865) and Op. 13 in G major (1867), Grieg successfully managed to introduce melodic and rhythmic idioms from Norwegian folk music. This was not a whimsical idea of his, but an attempt to show that nationally-coloured musical characteristics could be used effectively in all kinds of music. Nonetheless, Grieg frequently maintained that his aim was not focused on the specifically national, but on the universal aspects in his music. In a letter of 25 April 1881 to his biographer Aimar Grønvold he clarified his view: "I don't deny the exaggerated Norwegian passion of my youth but, as a modern artist, what I am striving for is that which is universal – or, more correctly, that which is individual. If the result is national, it is because the individual is national."[1] This view came to the fore in his third violin sonata, Op. 45 in C minor (1887), in which he transcended the boundaries of "Norwegianness", avoiding nearly all kinds of references to national music.

Grieg held his three violin sonatas in high regard and often performed them in collaboration with many renowned violinists on concert tours at home and abroad. On 9 January 1900, for example, he and Czech violinist Wilhelmina Neruda (Madame Hallé) played all the sonatas at a concert in Copenhagen. A few days after the concert, in a letter to his close friend Bjørnstjerne Bjørnson, a well-known Norwegian poet (honoured as a Nobel Laureate in literature, 1903), Grieg referred to his three violin sonatas as some of his best works, each of them representing an important period in his artistic development: "the first, naive, reflecting many antecedents; the second, national; and the third, with its wider horizons."[2]

Grieg's violin sonatas are included in Vol. 8 (1979) of *Edvard Grieg: Complete Works*, published by C. F. Peters 1978–95.

*

Only two years separated Grieg's first two violin sonatas, but 20 years elapsed between the second and the third. These two decades give ample evidence of the composer's creative power. The magnificent piano concerto in A minor, Op. 16 (1868) saw the light of day just one year after the second violin sonata; in addition to a large number of songs and piano pieces, Grieg also composed incidental music for Bjørnstjerne Bjørnson's drama *Sigurd Jorsalfar*, Op. 22 (1872), and for Henrik Ibsen's *Peer Gynt*, Op. 23 (1874–75), during this period. In the chamber-music field, he scaled the highest peaks of self-realization in the string quartet in G minor, Op. 27 (1878), and in the cello sonata in A minor, Op. 36 (1883), which was written for his elder brother John.

In 1884 Grieg realized that he needed a permanent home in Norway and started building the villa "Troldhaugen", five miles south of Bergen. It was completed in the spring of 1885 and appears to have given Grieg the emotional strength and *joie de vivre* necessary for the creation of new, significant compositions.

The first mention of a new violin sonata occurs in a letter of 25 July 1886 to Dr Max Abraham, the director of C. F. Peters in Leipzig: "I am now under way with a chamber-music work. Only the gods know when it will be finished, for I suffer the most unbelievable interruptions from foreign summer guests. Believe me, I am almost desperate."[3]

On 1 November, however, Grieg could tell Dr Abraham that not all visitors were so troublesome. A young Italian violin virtuoso had just a few days earlier come to see him at Troldhaugen: "Not only did she play the violin, she even drank champagne, both of which she did wonderfully! [...] Moreover, this fairy is also an extraordinarily lovely person, and if I shall once more perpetrate something for the violin, she is to be blamed for that."

The fairy, the 20-year-old Teresina Tua, highly enthused Grieg, and in a letter of 21 January 1887 he could tell his Bergen friend John Paulsen: "I have just written a violin sonata, which I shall now have the satisfaction of having lying in my desk until autumn before I shall hear it. For in the autumn I want to get away."[4]

Grieg declined a request from Max Abraham to send him the manuscript, for he wanted to hear it played before printing it. Grieg's letter has not been available, but his response can be deduced from a letter of 13 June 1887, in which Abraham writes: "You have given me two wounds in my heart by the message that you could not yet fulfil my heart's desire to let the world hear about your second piano concerto, and that you want to hear your violin composition before you would send it to me to be printed ..."

However, Grieg did not wait until autumn to hear the new sonata, for during the summer he played it at Troldhaugen with a Bergen violinist. His close friend Frants Beyer was present on this occasion. Upon hearing it played, Grieg realized that the sonata needed some reworking, which he decided to undertake in Leipzig. In a letter of 15 August, he disclosed his plans to Dr Abraham: "We plan to leave from here in mid-September, and if everything goes as we want, I shall look forward to a happy meeting with you at the end of October. I will then permit myself to bring you my new violin sonata, which – after having scrutinized it with a capable violinist – I would like to 'embellish' with the name of Edition Peters. There is only one drawback to this: are you now really inclined to print a new violin sonata of mine, since you already own one?"

In his response of 27 August, Abraham firmly expressed his wish to publish the new work: "My answer to that is: all good things come in three. I regard your two violin sonatas, besides the Concerto [Op. 16], as your most favoured compositions [...], and I am really looking forward to seeing number three."

Grieg left Troldhaugen in mid-September as planned and after a four-week regimen of curative treatment in Karlsbad (Karlovy Vary), he arrived in Leipzig on 20 October – according to notes in his account book from 1887.[5] Apart from a Berlin trip (27–31 December), he remained in Leipzig for nearly six months. That there is no correspondence between composer and publisher during this period is due to the fact that they were living in the same city. We may assume, however, that soon after his arrival in Leipzig Grieg delivered the sonata manuscript to his publisher so that the engraving process could get under way.

On 31 October Grieg reported in a letter to Frants Beyer that just a few days earlier a talented compatriot had come to see him and his wife Nina. It was Johan Halvorsen, who at that time was studying violin with the Russian violin virtuoso Adolph Brodsky, violin professor at the Leipzig Music Conservatory: "He [Halvorsen] makes a straightforward and good impression. [...] I hope to get an opportunity to know him better, but that is not so easy, for we do not frequent the same places. I can't stand the evening cafés of Leipzig [...]."[6] According to Grieg's account book another get-together with Halvorsen took place on 19 November ("Evening with Halvorsen – 17 German Marks"), probably after a strenuous rehearsal, to which Grieg refers in a letter of 22 November to Beyer: "The other evening he was up here and played through the sonata with me, and he did it with so much warmth and genuine artistry that I felt a wave of pride over the fact that he was my countryman."[7] Halvorsen, in a slightly differing version, refers to this event in an unpublished collection of autobiographical materials, written some decades later and preserved in the Nasjonalbiblioteket, Oslo (formerly Universitetsbiblioteket i Oslo). After mentioning that Brodsky was to premiere the sonata, he continues: "I was nonetheless the first one who played it. One day Grieg came to my room with the manuscript, and he wanted to hear how the violin part sounded. I think I was of some help to him at that time. We played the sonata through a couple of times, and I was completely enthralled by that beautiful work."[8] According to Halvorsen, both Grieg and the composer Christian Sinding made Brodsky's acquaintance at this time.

The last note in Grieg's account book from 1887 referring to Halvorsen is dated 20 December: "Halvorsen – 50 German Marks". In 1887, 50 German Marks amounted to a considerable sum of money and the sum was probably intended as an honorarium for Halvorsen's assistance. Grieg obviously appreciated his contribution but he never made any specific reference to it.

In the above-mentioned letter of 22 November to Beyer, Grieg tells of his first meeting with Adolph Brodsky: "I have just returned from the home of Professor Brodsky, Halvorsen's teacher, with whom I have played the new *Violin Sonata* of which you got such a poor impression last summer. I was as disappointed then as you were, but tonight (albeit after changing the shortcomings), I experienced a joy that is seldom granted to an artist. Brodsky played *absolutely incomparably*, and was himself completely enthusiastic about my work. I assure you, I didn't recognize it. It was indeed what I had intended, but I just didn't think my intentions could be made real."[9]

Brodsky wished to put the composition on the programme at one of his forthcoming chamber concerts in Leipzig, strongly requesting the composer's cooperation. Grieg accepted Brodsky's request, and in a letter of 3 December 1887 to his Danish colleague Nils Ravnkilde in Rome he gave the following comment: "I am a fool to do it, for I do not have the necessary strength, but he begged me, and he plays so irresistibly beautifully that I am completely captivated."[10]

The premiere performance of the C-minor sonata took place on 10 December in the Neues Gewandhaus, Leipzig. It was an immediate success, and the press reviews praised both Brodsky

and Grieg for a performance marked by warmth and fervour. On 11 December, Grieg reported to Beyer: "How he [Brodsky] played! After each movement there was prolonged applause, and two curtain calls after the finale."[11]

However, the notorious Eduard Bernsdorf – leading music critic of the influential Leipzig musical journal *Signale für die musikalische Welt* and a lifelong critic of Grieg's major works – again did his utmost to demean the composer, who was said to demonstrate a lack of talent which was plain to see in the tastelessness and musical trickery with which the sonata allegedly abounded!

A few weeks later there was another performance of the sonata at a dinner party given by the Brodsky family: "I have just come home from Brodsky's where we have been to dinner along with Tchaikovsky, who is still here with a young and *wonderfully brilliant* Russian pianist, [Wassily] Sapelnikov. Sinding and Halvorsen were also present, and we made music all the time. First, at Tchaikovsky's request, Brodsky and I played my new sonata. Then Sinding's quartet was tried out, with Sapelnikov at the piano, and lastly my *String Quartet*. Those fellows can really play! My God, what a sound!"[12]

The C-minor sonata was dedicated to the German painter Franz von Lenbach and published at the end of November 1887 by C. F. Peters.[13] It instantly became very popular and on 24 March 1888 Grieg could tell Beyer: "Just think: the new violin sonata, which has been in print for only a few months, has already sold about 1,500 copies. Dr Abraham says that is unique, including even Brahms."[14]

The work – written at about the same time when César Franck was composing his A-major sonata, but three years before Brahms's D-minor sonata saw the light of day – rapidly won acclaim throughout Europe. New printings appeared nearly every other year, and by 1906 the C. F. Peters publication records reveal that in the course of 19 years no fewer than 29,000 copies had been sold![15]

Grieg's previous violin sonatas had aroused interest not least because of their "Norwegianness", the national features tickling the ears of the international audience. Such is not the case with the C-minor sonata, which – "with its wider horizons" – has won acclaim solely on the strength of its innate musical qualities. The Belgian musicologist Ernest Closson in his book *Edvard Grieg et la musique scandinave* (1892, p. 40), seems to voice a representative opinion of the work: "It must be classed as belonging to the most inspired works ever written. [...] From beginning to end it is a marvel of inspiration, intelligence and independence."

The first movement, *Allegro molto ed appassionato* – Grieg's most successful exploitation of sonata form –, has a powerful, expressive intensity that comes clearly to the fore in the initial, poignant bars of the first part of the principal theme section, and smooth bridge passages between various thematic groups and a daring but consummately controlled harmonic style are striking features. A melodious secondary theme occurs in E-flat major (b. 59); the first segment of this theme is echoed in G-flat major in a characteristically Griegian manner (b. 79). The development section is virtually unique in Grieg's music. It starts *ppp* (b. 145), in an ethereal, lyrical vein in B-flat major, with an astonishing rhythmic augmentation of the initial two-bar motif of the principal theme, supported by a chromatically coloured bass line in the piano. After an intense crescendo the bass reaches the note E (b. 160), paving the way for a literal transposition of the preceding passage in A major, again beginning *ppp* (b. 163). Another abridged version of the augmention appears *forte* (b. 246), now *appassionato*, played with double stops by the violin in the home key. This passage leads to the recapitulation (b. 262). Very surprisingly, in b. 400 Grieg seems to start another development section by suddenly reintroducing the augmented version, now in A-flat major. However, the impression is deceptive. After 29 bars a *presto* coda, built on the initial two-bar motif, now starting pianissimo, brings the movement to a brilliant finish, characterized by poignant, modally coloured cadential fortissimo chords.[16]

The second movement, *Allegretto espressivo alla Romanza* (E major), which is in ternary form (ABA'), contains one of Grieg's most inspired creations. The A theme, introduced in the piano and later taken over by the violin, features marked interactions between a serenely lyrical melody and striking harmonic subtleties. A contrasting B section, *Allegro molto* (E minor), is built on dance-like four-bar phrases, somewhat related to the *halling*, a Norwegian folk dance. Harmonically interesting is a transitional passage at the end of the B section, where the chord progressions demonstrate an unusually luxuriant and brilliantly designed modulation (b. 189–217): from E minor, followed by a series of colourful chords over a chromatic bass line, the chord progression continues via E major and E-flat major, which precedes the A' section in E major. Even within the context of Grieg's richly faceted harmony, this passage is unique.

In the third movement, *Allegro animato* (C minor), the ethereal world of sound that prevailed at the end of the second movement is abruptly swept away by a rhythmically pregnant principal subject in the violin, with broken chords (open fifths) in the piano. This thematic group precedes a lyrical secondary theme in A-flat major, which is supported by a syncopated piano figure that gives the music a continuous push forward. The theme is based on a firmly chiselled motif that soon takes the form of a widely spun-out melody, steadily moving higher and higher as the dynamic tension increases.

After the exposition, Grieg gives us a great surprise. Instead of a fully-fledged development section, he introduces a few transitional bars bringing us straight into a regular recapitulation. Thus, the movement reveals a structural design that Grieg never employed in the finale of any other major work: a sonata form without a development section, or – as it may also be interpreted – a two-part form, AB–AB' plus a coda. The reason for the omission of a development is most likely the composer's subtle use of developmental devices in the exposition itself. In the recapitulation the B theme appears in C major – *Cantabile ed espressivo* – accompanied by rippling, harp-like broken chords in the piano. A turbulent *prestissimo* coda, where the sombre character of the original C-minor theme is transformed into jubilant C major, brings the work to a triumphant fortissimo conclusion.

The C-minor sonata, which has for more than a century occupied a prominent place in the repertoire of many of the world's leading violinists, proves Grieg's ability to write chamber music "with wider horizons". Compared to the two preceding violin sonatas it shows a more profound concentration and at the same time a striking fusion of lyrical expressiveness and dark-hued dramatic pathos. The C-minor sonata is a sterling contribution to Romantic chamber music.

Kristiansand, November 2011

Professor Finn Benestad
Editor of Edvard Grieg: Complete Works, vol. 8

[1] Finn Benestad and Dag Schjelderup-Ebbe: *Edvard Grieg. The Man and the Artist* (English translation by William H. Halverson and Leland B. Sateren), Lincoln and London 1988, p. 332.

[2] *Ibid.*, p. 73.

[3] The complete correspondence between Grieg and the C. F. Peters directors, Dr Max Abraham and his successor, Dr Henri Hinrichsen, is published in *Edvard Grieg. Briefwechsel mit dem Musikverlag C. F. Peters 1863–1907* (edited by Finn Benestad & Hella Brock), Frankfurt/M. 1997. The English translation of the quotation is given in Benestad and Schjelderup-Ebbe: *Op. cit.*, p. 276.

[4] Benestad and Schjelderup-Ebbe: *Op. cit.*, p. 276.

[5] Grieg kept a minute account of his expenses, particularly when staying abroad: stamps, paper, taxis, railway tickets, cakes, dinners, theatre and opera tickets and other kinds of entertainment. Grieg's account books are preserved in the Bergen Offentlige Bibliotek.

[6] 230 Grieg letters to Frants Beyer, written in Norwegian, are published in *Edvard Grieg. Brev til Frants Beyer 1872–1907* (edited by Finn Benestad and Bjarne Kortsen), Oslo 1993. Quotation on p. 108.

[7] 50 Grieg letters to Beyer are given in English translation in *Edvard Grieg. Letters to Colleagues and Friends* (some 500 letters selected and edited by Finn Benestad; translated by William H. Halverson), Columbus, Ohio 2000. Quotation on p. 48.

[8] Halvorsen's collection bears the title *"Hvad jeg husker fra mit Liv (Til mine Barn)"* [What I remember from my life (To my children)]. See also Benestad and Schjelderup-Ebbe: *Op. cit.*, p. 276.

[9] *Edvard Grieg: Letters to Colleagues and Friends*, pp. 47–48.

[10] *Edvard Grieg. Brev i utvalg 1862–1907*, vol. II (selected and edited by Finn Benestad), Oslo 1998, p. 226.

[11] Benestad and Schjelderup-Ebbe: *Op. cit.*, p. 277.

[12] See letter of 29 January 1888 to Beyer in *Edvard Grieg: Letters to Colleagues and Friends*, p. 51. The relation between Grieg and Brodsky soon developed into a lifelong, close friendship. For Grieg's funeral in 1907, Brodsky came from Manchester to Bergen to honour his friend by attending the ceremony and playing in an orchestra set up for the occasion by Halvorsen.

[13] *Edvard Grieg. Thematisch-Bibliographisches Werkverzeichnis*, ed. Dan Fog †, Kirsti Grinde and Øyvind Norheim, Frankfurt/Main, 2008, p. 208. A wealth of interesting materials is documented in Rolf Christian Erdahl's dissertation (1994): *Edvard Grieg's sonatas for stringed instrument and piano: Performance indications of the primary source materials*, Ann Arbor, Michigan 2001. A comprehensive investigation of Grieg's chamber music is given in Finn Benestad & Dag Schjelderup-Ebbe: *Edvard Grieg. Chamber Music: Nationalism – Universality – Individuality*, Oslo 1993.

[14] Benestad and Schjelderup-Ebbe: *Edvard Grieg. The Man and the Artist*, p. 277.

[15] Information kindly given by Klaus Burmeister (Dresden), former chief editor of C. F. Peters, Leipzig.

[16] Some musicologists interpret the A-flat major section in b. 400 as the opening of the coda; cf. Patrick Dinslage's discussion in his in-depth study: "Zu Edvard Griegs dritter Violinsonate opus 45 in c-moll. Anmerkungen zu Harmonik und Form", in *Studia Musicologica Norvegica*, No. 25, 1999, pp. 108–123, here p. 113.

Sonate

c-Moll · C minor

I

Edvard Grieg (1843–1907)
Opus 45
Herausgegeben von Finn Benestad

Allegro molto ed appassionato ♩. = 116

4

33160

8

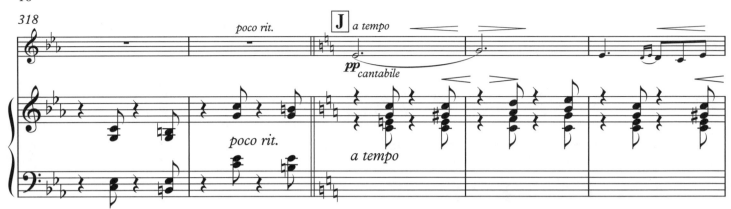

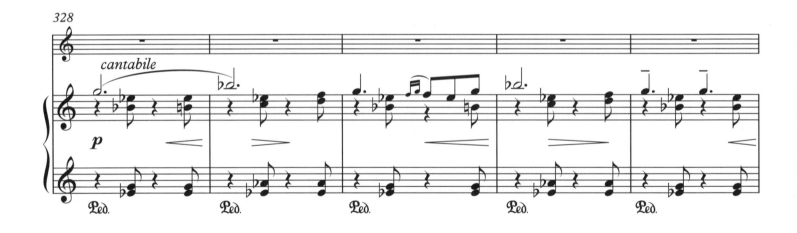

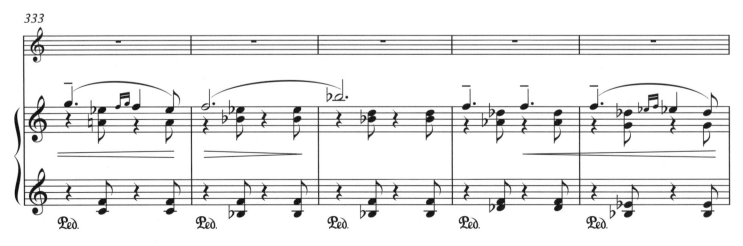

358
f
363
dim.
poco sosten.
Ped.
K
369
a tempo
ppp
Ped. una corda
374
p cantabile e tranquillo
pp tranquillo
cresc. poco a poco
tre corde

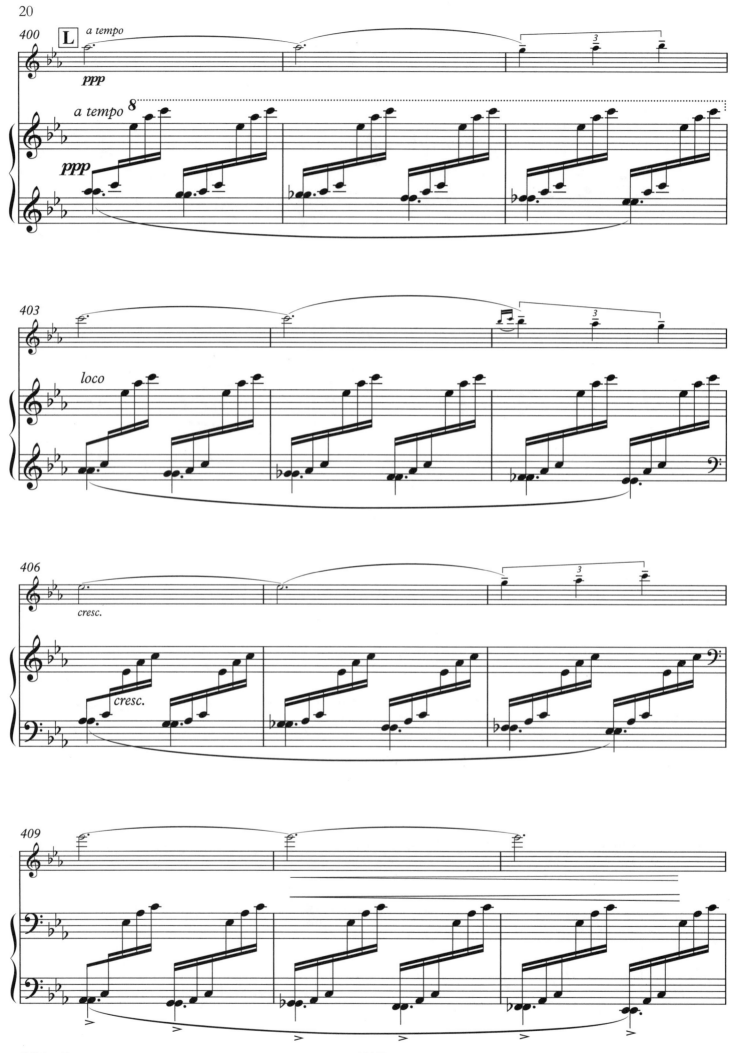

II

Allegretto espressivo alla Romanza ♩ = 72

24

33160

26

33160

Violino

Sonate

c-Moll · C minor

I

Edvard Grieg (1843–1907)
Opus 45
Herausgegeben von Finn Benestad*)

Allegro molto ed appassionato ♩. = 116

*) Fingersätze und Strichbezeichnungen von Johan Halvorsen (1864–1935) gemäß der von Grieg autorisierten Erstausgabe (Quelle SC, vgl. Revisionsbericht).
Fingering and bowing by Johan Halvorsen (1864–1935) in accordance with the first edition, authorized by Grieg (Source SC, cf. Editorial Commentary).

Edition Peters Nr. 11313

33160

II

Allegretto espressivo alla Romanza ♩ = 72

III

MUSIK FÜR VIOLINE / MUSIC FOR VIOLIN

VIOLINE SOLO

J. S. BACH 6 Sonaten u. Partiten BWV 1001–1006 (Rostal). .EP 9852

FISCHER Basics / Practice. Etüden (engl.) . . . . EP 7440/7578

GENZMER Sonate (1983/84, rev. 1991). . . . . .EP 8683

HALVORSEN Slåtter, Norwegische Bauerntänze . . . . .EP 3083

NIELSEN Präludium und Thema mit Variationen op. 48. . . .EP 3817

PAGANINI Sonate A-Dur, Erstausgabe, Urtext (Jelden). . .EP 11037
– 24 Capricen op. 1 (Hertel) . . . . .EP 9979

REGER 6 Präludien und Fugen op. 131a . . . . .EP 3968
– Präludium e-Moll op. posth. . . . . .EP 3968d

RODE 24 Capricen (Davisson) . . . . EP 281a

R. STRAUSS Orchesterstudien (Prill), Band I und II. . . . EP 4189a/b

TELEMANN 12 Fantasien (TWV 40:14–25)
für Violine ohne Bass (Fechner/Thiemann). . . . . .EP 9365

TÜÜR Confession. . . . . .EP 11219

VIEUXTEMPS 6 Konzertetüden op. 16 (Arbós) . . . . .EP 2564
– 6 Morceaux op. 55 (Drüner) .EP 8356

WIENIAWSKI Études-Caprices op. 18 . . . . .EP 3395
– L'École moderne op. 10 . . . . .EP 3368

2–3 VIOLINEN

ALDRIDGE Carolinian Dances .EP 68176

BOCCHERINI Duos op. 5: G, E, f (GV 63–65) (Sitt) . . . . . .EP 3338

GENZMER Studieren und Musizieren für 2 Violinen (E. Keller)
– Teil 1–2: 26 Duos / Teil 3: Sonatine / Teil 4: 12 Duos . . EP 8432a/b/c

HAYDN 3 Duos op. 99 (nach Hob. III:40; III:20; III:23). . . .EP 3303

PACHELBEL Kanon u. Gigue f. 3 Violinen u. B. c. (Gurgel). . .EP 9846

REGER 3 Duos op. 131b: e, d, A . . . . EP 3969d/e/f

SPOHR 3 Duette op. 3 / 2 Duette op. 9 . . . . EP 1086a/b
– 3 Duette op. 39 / 2 Duette op. 67 . . . . EP 1086c/d

TELEMANN 6 Kanonische Sonaten TWV 40:118–123
für 2 Violinen (C. Herrmann). . . . . .EP 4394

VIOTTI Duos op. 29 (C. Herrmann) . . . . .EP 1087a

VIVALDI Konzert a-Moll op. 3 Nr. 8 (RV 522)
für 2 Violinen und Streicher, Ausgabe für 1–2 Violinen
und Klavier nach dem Urtext (Eller/Erben) . . . . .EP 9458a

VIOLINE UND KLAVIER / CEMBALO

J. B. ACCOLAY Concerto a-Moll (»Concertino I«) (Matz) . .EP 11249

C. Ph. E. BACH Sonate g f. Fl. (Vl.) u. Cemb./Klavier, (früher
J. S. Bach zugeschrieben, BWV 1020) (Gurgel/Jacobi) . . . . . .EP 9856

J. S. BACH Sonaten h, A, E (BWV 1014–1016). . . . . .EP 4591a
– Sonaten c, f, G (BWV 1017–1019) (Stiehler/Schleifer) . . . .EP 4591b
– Sonaten G, e, c (BWV 1021, 1023, 1024)
für Violine und Basso continuo (H. Keller) . . . . .EP 4591c

BEETHOVEN Sonaten (J. Joachim)
– Bd. I op. 12/1–3; 23; 24 (Frühlingssonate) . . . . .EP 3031a
– Bd. II op. 30/1–3; 47 (Kreutzersonate); 96 . . . . .EP 3031b

BOCCHERINI Sonate B-Dur op. 5/3 (GV 27) (Vorholz) . . . EP 8079

BRAHMS Sonaten op. 78, 100, 108 (Flesch/Schnabel) . . . . . .EP 3900

CLEMENTI 3 Sonatinen op. 36/1–3 (orig. f. Klavier), mit
hinzukomponierter Violinstimme von Max Reger (F. Matz) . . .EP 11091

CORELLI Sonaten D, F, e (op. 5 Nr. 1, 4, 8) (Klengel) . . . . .EP 3836a
– Sonaten C, g, A (op. 5 Nr. 3, 5, 9) (Klengel) . . . . .EP 3836b

DEBUSSY Sonate (Garay) . . . . .EP 9121

DVOŘÁK Sonatine G-Dur op. 100 (Vorholz). . . . . .EP 9363
– Romantische Stücke op. 75 (Gurgel/Thiemann). . . . . .EP 9824

FAURÉ Sonate Nr. 1 A-Dur op. 13 (Howat) . . . . .EP 7487
– Sonate Nr. 2 e-Moll op. 108 (van Amerongen). . . . . .EP 9891a
– Après un rêve (Howat) . . . . .EP 7481

FRANCK Sonate A-Dur (Jacobson) . . . . .EP 3742

GRIEG Sonaten für Violine und Klavier, Urtext,
Neuausgaben nach GGA (Benestad)
– Sonate Nr. 1 F-Dur op. 8 . . . . .EP 11311
– Sonate Nr. 2 G-Dur op. 13 . . . . .EP 11312
– Sonate Nr. 3 c-Moll op. 45 . . . . .EP 11313

HÄNDEL Sonaten für Violine und B. c. (Davisson/Ramin)
– – Bd. I Sonaten A, a, F (HWV 361, 368, 370). . . . . .EP 4157a
– – Bd. II Sonaten D, A, E (HWV 371, 372, 373) . . . . .EP 4157b
– Sonaten für Violine und B. c. (Burrows)
– – Bd. I Sonaten HWV 359a, 361, 364a, 367a, 372, 373 . . . .EP 7315
– – Bd. II Sonaten und Stücke HWV 288, 358, 368,
370, 371, 406, 407, 408, 412 . . . . .EP 7316

HAYDN Sonaten F, es, G, B, G (Hob. XV:17, 31, 32, 38;
Hob. XVI, 43bis) (K. H. Köhler) . . . . .EP 9017
– Sonate G (nach Hob. III:81) . . . . .EP 190a

JANSCHINOW Concerto op. 35 im russischen Stil . . . . . . .EP 4706

KOMAROWSKI Konzert Nr. 1 e-Moll . . . . .EP 4747
– Konzert Nr. 2 A-Dur. . . . . .EP 4780

KÜCHLER Concertino D-Dur op. 15 (im Stil von Vivaldi)
für Violine und Klavier (Schülerkonzert 1. und 3. Lage),
Neuausgabe (F. Matz) . . . . .EP 11029

MENDELSSOHN BARTHOLDY Sonate f-Moll op. 4 . . . . .EP 1732
– Sonate F-Dur, Erstausgabe (Y. Menuhin) . . . . .EP 6075

MONTI Czardas (Csárdás) (Bütow). . . . . .EP 11208

MOZART Sonaten (Flesch/Schnabel)
– Bd. I KV 296, 301–306, 376, 377 . . . . .EP 3315a

MOZART / HERZOGENBERG Rondo a-Moll KV 511,
bearbeitet für Violine und kleines Orchester (Herzogenberg)
Ausgabe für Violine und Klavier (Erstveröffentlichung). . . .EP 11021

NOVÁČEK Perpetuum mobile (Davisson). . . . . .EP 2786

PFITZNER Sonate e-Moll op. 27. . . . . .EP 3620

RAFF Cavatine D-Dur op. 85 Nr. 3
(mit: Vieuxtemps, Rêverie; Wieniawski, Légende) . . . . .EP 3383

REGER 6 ausgewählte kleine Stücke (op. 79/1, 2, 3; op. 87/1;
Romanze G; Petite Caprice g) (Thiemann). . . . . .EP 9105

RIEDING (Schüler-)Konzert h-Moll op. 35 (1. Lage)
für Violine und Klavier, Neuausgabe (F. Matz) . . . . .EP 11025

SAINT-SAËNS Sonate op. 75 (Thiemann) . . . . .EP 9291
– Havanaise op. 83 . . . . .EP 9292

SCHUBERT Sonatinen D-Dur, a-Moll, g-Moll op. posth. 137,
Urtext (Burmeister). . . . . .EP 11099

SCHUMANN Sonaten a-Moll op.105, d-Moll op. 121 . . . . . .EP 2367
– Fantasiestücke op. 73 / Märchenbilder op. 113 . . EP 2366b/ EP 2372

SEITZ (Schüler-)Konzert D-Dur op. 22 (1. Lage)
für Violine und Klavier, Neuausgabe (F. Matz). . . . . .EP 11028

TELEMANN 6 Sonatinen (TWV 41: A2, B2, D2, G3, E1, F1)
mit Vc. ad lib. (Maertens/Bernstein) . . . . .EP 9096

TESSARINI Konzert G-Dur op. 1 Nr. 3 für Violine u. Str., Ausg.
f. Vl. u. Klav. (Schülerkonzert 1. u. 3. Lage) (F. Matz) . . . . .EP 11027

VERACINI 12 Sonaten (1716) mit B. c., 4 Bde. (Kolneder). . EP 4965a-d

VIVALDI Die vier Jahreszeiten op. 8 Nr. 1–4 (Kolneder)
– Nr. 1 Der Frühling RV 269 / Nr. 2 Der Sommer RV 315 . . EP 9055a/b
– Nr. 3 Der Herbst RV 293 / Nr. 4 Der Winter RV 297 . . . EP 9055c/d

C. F. PETERS · FRANKFURT/M. · LEIPZIG · LONDON · NEW YORK
www.edition-peters.de · www.edition-peters.com

33160

III

Allegro animato ♩ = 104

Revisionsbericht

Der im Folgenden wiedergegebene Revisionsbericht entstammt im Kern der *Edvard-Grieg-Gesamtausgabe* (GGA), herausgegeben vom Edvard-Grieg-Komitee · Oslo, hier Band 8: *Sonaten für Violine und Klavier* (und weitere Kammermusikwerke), herausgegeben von Finn Benestad (Frankfurt/M. 1979). Der Text wurde für die vorliegende Ausgabe redaktionell überarbeitet und inhaltlich erweitert.

Seit Erscheinen von GGA, Band 8, im Jahr 1979 ist in großer Zahl neues Forschungsmaterial zu Grieg und seiner Musik zutage befördert worden. Rund 3000 Grieg-Briefe, umfassende biographische Abhandlungen, analytische Bücher und Aufsätze, Tage- und Haushaltsbücher wurden seitdem publiziert und gewährten neue Einblicke in Griegs Leben und Werk. Jüngere Beiträge zur Biographik, die im Zusammenhang mit der c-Moll-Sonate stehen, werden in den Fußnoten im Vorwort der vorliegenden Ausgabe referiert.

Untenstehende Angaben zum *Quellenmaterial* wurden gemäß neueren Erkenntnissen des Herausgebers aktualisiert. Diese ergaben sich vor allem aus einer stärkeren Differenzierung der Druckquelle C, die erst durch die Auswertung der historischen Auflagebücher des Peters-Verlages möglich wurde. Nicht zuletzt hierdurch konnte auch Quelle S, der separaten Violinstimme aus C, eine größere editorische Relevanz zuerkannt werden, als dies noch für die Partiturfassung in GGA der Fall war.

In den abschließenden, dreiteilig angelegten *Einzelanmerkungen* ist der erweiterte Quellenbestand berücksichtigt.

*

Die *Sonate für Violine und Klavier* Nr. 3 c-Moll op. 45 ist Edvard Griegs letzte Violinsonate. Sie wurde im Herbst und Winter 1886 auf „Troldhaugen" bei Bergen komponiert. Die Erstausgabe erschien 1887 bei C. F. Peters, Leipzig. Das Werk ist dem deutschen Porträtmaler Franz von Lenbach (1836–1904) gewidmet.

Die Uraufführung der Sonate fand am 10. Dezember 1887 im Neuen Gewandhaus, Leipzig, statt. Es spielte der Geiger Adolph Brodsky (1851–1929), vom Komponisten begleitet.

Das Quellenmaterial

A:

Autograph der Klavierpartitur in Bergen Offentlige Bibliotek (Bergen Öffentliche Bibliothek). Ohne separate Violinstimme.

Das Manuskript (Ms.) umfasst 22 lose Blätter mit vier vorgedruckten, vollständigen Notensystemen (Violinstimme und Klavierstimme) auf jeder Seite. Das Firmenzeichen des Papiers ist *C. A. Klemm. C. N° 7*. Das Titelblatt und seine Rückseite sind nicht paginiert, S. [25a] ist nicht beschrieben. Nach S. 39 folgen zwei gleichfalls unbeschriebene und unpaginierte Seiten. Das Format ist 35,6 x 26,2 cm.

Das Titelblatt zeigt folgende Aufschrift mit Tinte: *F. v. Lenbach / gewidmet. / Sonate / für Pianoforte und Violine / (N° 3, C moll) / von / Edvard Grieg. / op. 45.* Am Kopf des Titelblatts ist mit Blaustift, nicht von Griegs Hand, hinzugefügt: *Bis 19/11* und *Nr. 54347*; unten auf der Seite findet sich folgende Bleistift-

notiz, auch diese nicht von Grieg geschrieben: *Fortsetzung zu 7178 / Violinstimme folgt / 15/11.87.* In ähnlicher Schrift steht auf S. 1: *Buchstaben einziehen?* S. 18: *12/11/87*; und auf S. 39: *15/11/87. Kühn und schwungvoll, hab's gern so.* Das Ms. ist klar geschrieben und deutlich lesbar.

Satzeinteilung:

S. 1–18:   I.   *Allegro molto ed appassionato.* M. M. $\downarrow$ = 116

S. 19–25:   II. *Allegretto espressivo alla Romanza.* [ohne Metronomangabe]

S. 26–39: III. *Allegro animato.* $\downarrow$ = [die Metronomzahl fehlt]

Korrekturen:

Überall im Autograph finden sich Zusätze mit Rotstift oder mit Bleistift. Die meisten betreffen Pedalisierungsangaben.

Herkunft:

Das Ms. war Stichvorlage für die Erstausgabe. Mehrere Jahrzehnte gehörte es zu einer privaten Sammlung in London, in die es auf unbekanntem Weg gelangt war. Mit finanzieller Unterstützung von Kavlis almennyttige fond und G. C. Rieber & Co., Bergen, konnte das Autograph im Jahr 2005 über das Musikantiquariat Dr. Ulrich Drüner, Stuttgart, für die Bergen Offentlige Bibliotek erworben werden, der Kaufpreis betrug £ 40.000.[1]

B:

The Royal Northern College of Music, Manchester (das frühere Royal Manchester College of Music) besitzt Griegs Autograph einer separaten Violinstimme der c-Moll-Sonate. Die eigenhändige Niederschrift befand sich spätestens seit Dezember 1897 im Besitz Adolph Brodskys, der das Manuskript später dem Royal Manchester College of Music vermachte.

Das Titelblatt zeigt folgende Aufschrift in Griegs Handschrift: *Ich bezeuge hiermit, dass: / Diese Stimme ist nicht etwa von / Brodsky geschrieben, sondern von seinem / Freund und kolossaler* [!] *Verehrer / Edvard Grieg / Manchester 19/12/97 / Violino.*

Trotz der eigenhändigen Datierung bleibt es letztlich ungewiss, wann die Niederschrift von B erfolgte; als Stichvorlage für den Erstdruck (1887) diente das Ms. jedenfalls nicht, da es keine Stechereintragungen aufweist. B steht offenkundig in direktem Zusammenhang mit jenem autographen Ms. der Solostimme, das Grieg von Troldhaugen nach Leipzig mitbrachte und dort im November 1887 zunächst mit dem Geiger Johan Halvorsen studierte (siehe Vorwort), bevor er es – mit Änderungen versehen – als separate Stichvorlage beim Verlag einreichte (*Violinstimme folgt*, siehe rechts, Quelle C). Allem Anschein nach ist B eine Abschrift bzw. Reinschrift dieser (verschollenen) Stichvorlage, in welche die von Halvorsen nachträglich vorgeschlagenen und von Grieg sanktionierten Änderungen eingeflossen waren.

Die Frage, wann und zu welcher Begebenheit Grieg das Ms. an Adolph Brodsky weitergab, bleibt offen: ob als Zeichen der Wertschätzung für dessen brillantes Spiel bei der Uraufführung der Sonate (10. Dezember 1887) oder – erst zehn Jahre später – als großmütige Geste während eines Besuches im Hause Brodsky in Manchester. Wie dem auch gewesen sein mag, am 19. Dezember 1897 brachte Grieg den oben zitierten autographen Widmungsvermerk auf dem Titelblatt der Handschrift an.

C:

Erstausgabe, erschienen bei C. F. Peters, Leipzig 1887, Platten-Nr. 7178 (Edition Peters Nr. 2414), 45 + 11 Seiten, Peters-Editionsformat.

Das Titelblatt zeigt folgenden Text: *Franz von Lenbach / gewidmet / Sonate / (C moll) / für Pianoforte und Violine / von / EDVARD GRIEG / Op. 45. / Eigenthum des Verlegers. / LEIPZIG / C. F. PETERS. / F. Baumgarten, del.*

Als Quelle wurden folgende Druckexemplare herangezogen:

1. Auflage (Erstdruck)[2], November 1887 (im Folgenden: C_1). Fundort: Nasjonalbiblioteket (Nationalbibliothek) Oslo. Exemplar mit eigenhändiger Widmung an Johan Halvorsen: *Til min kjære Ven og Landsmand Johan Halvorsen fra Din heng. Edvard Grieg. Leipzig Dcbr 87.* („Für meinen lieben Freund und Landsmann Johan Halvorsen von Deinem ergebenen Edvard Grieg. Leipzig Dcbr 87.").

2. Auflage, Dezember 1887 (im Folgenden: C). Fundort: Bergen Offentlige Bibliotek (Bergen Öffentliche Bibliothek). Exemplar mit eigenhändiger Widmung an Nina Grieg: *Med kjærlig Julehilsen fra Din Edv.* („Mit liebevollem Weihnachtsgruß von Deinem Edv.").

Die Erstauflage mit 500 Exemplaren, gedruckt in den letzten Novembertagen 1887, war ein augenblicklicher Erfolg. Bereits im Dezember desselben Jahres folgte mit 1000 Druckexemplaren die 2. Auflage, im Mai 1888 in gleicher Höhe die 3. Auflage. Zahlreiche Nachdrucke schlossen sich an, so dass die c-Moll-Sonate es bis 1906 auf die geradezu unglaubliche Absatzzahl von 29.000 Exemplaren brachte. Über alle Druckauflagen hinweg blieb die originale Plattennummer (7178) erhalten, eine Neuausgabe erschien zu Griegs Lebenszeit nicht.

C, die 2. Druckauflage, zeigt gegenüber dem Erstdruck (C_1) eine große Zahl kleinerer Korrekturen (z. B. hinsichtlich Dynamik, Bogensetzung und Pedalisierung), die auf Veranlassung oder in Abstimmung mit dem Komponisten erfolgt sein müssen. In geringerem Maß als die Partitur erfuhr auch die separate Solostimme (S) beim Übergang von SC_1 zu SC kleinere Veränderungen (so wurde z. B. im 3. Satz, T. 37, das ursprüngliche *ces²* zu *c²* geändert und in einigen Takten der Fingersatz modifiziert). SC_1/SC zeigen jedoch in allen drei Sätzen zahlreiche Abweichungen von der Violinstimme in der Partitur (Vl), vor allem bei Angaben zur Dynamik. Diese Abweichungen sind dadurch zu erklären, dass für SC_1/SC als Stichvorlage nicht A diente, sondern jene (verschollene) Stichvorlage, auf die in A durch die Worte *Violinstimme folgt* hingewiesen wurde. Dahinter stand vermutlich Griegs Absicht, die Violinstimme vor Drucklegung noch einmal zu revidieren und hierfür den Geiger Johan Halvorsen (vgl. Quelle B) zu Rate zu ziehen. Die letztlich zum Druck gelangte Stimme SC_1 blieb – abgesehen von den erwähnten kleinen Änderungen in SC – in allen Folgeauflagen unverändert. Eine nachträgliche Angleichung des Violinparts in der Partitur (Vl) an SC_1/SC erfolgte allerdings nicht; offenbar sah der Verlag keine Notwendigkeit hierzu, zumal Vl keine Notenfehler enthielt. Aber auch Grieg selbst scheint die Angleichung nicht nachdrücklich eingefordert zu haben. Bedauerlicherweise sind zu Fragen der Drucklegung keine Briefbelege überliefert, da Grieg in jenen Wochen Ende 1887 in Leipzig wohnte und jederzeit in direkten Kontakt zu

C. F. Peters treten konnte. Auch Korrekturabzüge, die den Publikationsprozess weiter erhellen könnten, sind nicht erhalten.

Quelle C zeigt den Notentext in einem vom Komponisten genehmigten Status; C (Kl-s) war folgerichtig Hauptquelle für die Edition der c-Moll-Sonate in GGA. Die vorliegende Ausgabe basiert auf GGA, misst aber der auf Grieg und Halvorsen zurückgehenden Lesart SC für den Violinpart stärkeres Gewicht bei und räumt ihr im Regelfall editorische Priorität ein, da sie im Vergleich zu Vl vollständiger und differenzierter ausgeführt ist, vor allem in Bezug auf die Dynamik. Somit spiegelt SC, obwohl nicht frei von Stichfehlern und Ungenauigkeiten, die von Grieg letztlich gewünschte Werkgestalt am deutlichsten wider.

*

Abkürzungen und Vorbemerkung zu den Einzelanmerkungen:

GGA: *Grieg-Gesamtausgabe* (hier Band 8, zugleich Grundlage der vorliegenden Edition).

A, B und C bzw. C_1: die oben genannten Quellen.

Kl–s: beide Stimmen (Violine und Klavier) der Klavierpartitur.

Kl: die Klavierstimme der Klavierpartitur.

Vl: die Violinstimme der Klavierpartitur.

S: die separate Solostimme in C (= SC) oder C_1 (= SC_1).

Bei spielpraktisch relevanten Abweichungen zwischen SC und Vl in den Quellen übernimmt die vorliegende Ausgabe, anders als GGA, die favorisierte Lesart SC auch in die Partitur. Die Neuausgabe kommt damit – erstmals in der Edition Peters – der von Grieg mutmaßlich intendierten Gestalt des Violinparts auch innerhalb der Partitur nach. Diese Übernahme kann ohne Einzelnachweis geschehen, da die (neue) Druckfassung von Vl durch die von Grieg autorisierte Lesart SC legitimiert und die bisherige Druckfassung jederzeit aus GGA zu ersehen ist. In den Einzelanmerkungen des Revisionsberichtes wird jedoch nachgewiesen, wo die vorliegende Ausgabe von SC abweicht, indem sie die Defizite dieser Quelle korrigiert oder präzisiert (Abschnitt c). Änderungen in Kl, die sich als Folge einer Änderung in Vl ergeben, werden in Abschnitt b genannt.

Da SC_1 und SC nahezu identisch sind, wird im Folgenden in der Regel nur auf SC verwiesen.

SC_1, SC und B enthalten Fingersatzangaben, besonders im 1. Satz. In B stehen die meisten von ihnen in Klammern. Die vermutlich von Halvorsen stammenden Fingersätze wurden von Grieg gebilligt; die vorliegende Edition übernimmt sie – mitunter geringfügig korrigiert – in die separate Violinstimme.

---

[1] Freundliche Auskunft von Siren Steen, Kuratorin der Grieg-Sammlung (Griegsamligen), Bergen Offentlige Bibliotek. Der Herausgeber dankt Siren Steen für vielfache Unterstützung im Zusammenhang mit der vorliegenden Ausgabe.

[2] Die Stadien von Erstdruck und Folgeauflagen samt bestehender Abweichungen wurden dankenswerterweise von Øyvind Norheim verifiziert, einem der Herausgeber des *Grieg-Werkverzeichnisses* (siehe Vorwort, Anm. 13), das im Jahr 2008 nach Band 20 der GGA als deren Abschluss erschien.

Einzelanmerkungen

Partitur (a) · Klavierpart (b) · Violinpart (c)

a) Partitur

Die folgenden Einzelanmerkungen werden gemäß GGA, Band 8, wiedergegeben, hier geringfügig überarbeitet und durch einige zusätzliche Lesartangaben (betreffend Quellen A und C_1) ergänzt. Jene Anmerkungen in GGA, die sich allein auf Lesart-Divergenzen zwischen Partitur und SC (Violinpart) bezogen, können unberücksichtigt bleiben, da die vorliegende Ausgabe – anders als GGA – in der Partitur direkt die Lesart SC wiedergibt.

I. Satz: *Allegro molto ed appassionato* M.M. ♩ = 116.

Takt / Instrument / Kommentar

5	Vl	In C fehlt ♮ vor der 2. Note.
67–78	Kl	A hat unvollständige Pedalisierungsangaben. GGA folgt C. Grieg hat sicherlich während der Korrektur ergänzt und verbessert.
79	Kl	In A und C_1 fehlt *una corda*.
87	Kl	In A und C_1 fehlt *tre corde* (vgl. auch T. 348).
103–107	Kl	Die Pedalangaben in A sind falsch platziert. Grieg hat sie vermutlich bei der Korrektur verbessert.
114	Kl	In A fehlt *tre corde*.
114–163	Kl	Sämtliche Pedalisierungsangaben (℘ed. und ✳) fehlen in A und C_1 (vgl. oben T. 67–78).
116–117	Kl–s	C hat *molto cresc. poco a poco*; das *molto* ist hier unmotiviert und gehört nach T. 121 (vgl. auch T. 378).
129–143	Kl–s	In A hat Kl in T. 130 ⟨ ⟩. Für Vl fehlen in A sämtliche Gabeln im angegebenen Bereich.
135–136	Kl–s	A und C haben *cresc. molto e ritard.* In GGA *cresc. molto e poco ritard.* entsprechend B und SC.
178, 184	Kl	℘ed.-Angaben fehlen in A und C_1.
206	Vl	*tranquillo* nicht in B.
249	Vl	A und C_1 haben jeweils nur die oberen Noten, in C korrigiert.
261	Vl	In C fehlen Akzente.
284	Vl	In A fehlt ♮ vor der 2. Note.
325	Vl	In A und C_1 fehlen Vorschlagsnoten.
328–339	Kl	In A keine Pedalisierungsangaben.
340	Kl	In A und C_1 fehlt *una corda*.
348	Kl	℘ed. und *tre corde* nicht in A.
377	Kl	C hat unmotivierte ⟨ .
382–385	Kl–s	*molto* in C, T. 385, steht falsch. Es gehört zu ⟨ in T. 382/383 entsprechend SC.
386	Vl	In C fehlt der Bindebogen.
390–398	Kl–s	Die dynamischen Zeichen in C stimmen nicht mit denen in A und B überein. GGA folgt diesen Quellen.
418–423	Vl	In C kein > über der 1. Note in jedem Takt.
430	Kl–s	Keine Metronomangabe in A.
433	Vl	In C kein > über der 1. Note.
433	Kl	Rechte Hand: A und C_1 haben als Unternoten *d-des*, in C zu *des-des* korrigiert.

II. Satz: *Allegretto espressivo alla Romanza* M.M. ♩ = 72.

Takt / Instrument / Kommentar

1	Kl–s	In A fehlt die Metronomangabe.
14	Kl	A hat *f*. GGA folgt C.
25	Kl	A und C_1 haben ein Arpeggiozeichen durch beide Systeme. GGA folgt C, was der Parallelstelle T. 27 am nächsten kommt und wahrscheinlich eine Korrektur von Grieg ist.
29, 33, 37	Kl	A hat ein Arpeggiozeichen nur für linke Hand, in C wahrscheinlich eine Korrektur von Grieg.
60–61	Vl	C hat *dolcissimo*. In GGA *dolce* entsprechend SC.
73	Vl	In C fehlt *p*.
78	Vl	In C fehlt *più agitato*.
86	Kl–s	In C fehlt *rit*.
89	Kl–s	In A fehlt die Metronomangabe.
89	Vl	In C *ma marcato* statt *ma poco marcato*.
97, 101	Vl	A hat - statt >.
105	Vl	C hat *poco marcato* statt *p ma poco marcato*.
105	Kl–s	In A und C fehlt *a tempo* in beiden Stimmen.
128	Kl	In C fehlt ⟩.
139	Kl	Hinsichtlich der dynamischen Zeichen stimmen die Quellen nicht überein. GGA gibt *ffz* an entsprechend T. 143 in C. Dies ist eine bei Grieg häufig vorkommende Bezeichnung.
146–147	Kl	In C eine falsch platzierte ⟩. In GGA ist das Zeichen entsprechend Vl nach T. 147–148 gerückt.
156	Vl	In C fehlt ⟨.
160	Kl	In C fehlt ⟩.
164	Vl	In C fehlt ⟨ (vgl. T. 156).
164	Kl	Linke Hand: In A und C_1 fehlen übergebundene ♩-Note *h* und Haltebogen von T. 163.
175	Kl	In A fehlt > über der 1. Note.
180	Kl	Linke Hand: A und C_1 haben als Oberstimme ♩-Note a-c^1.
194	Vl	In C fehlt *espressivo*.
225	Vl	In C fehlt *dolce*.
265	Vl	In C fehlt *ppp*.

III. Satz: *Allegro animato* ♩ = 104

Takt / Instrument / Kommentar

1	Kl–s	In A fehlt die Metronomangabe.
6	Kl	In A fehlt das Staccatozeichen unter g^1 im unteren System.
19, 217	Vl	A hat , sicher eine Korrektur von Grieg.
22	Kl	In A und C_1 fehlt *una corda*.
25, 30	Kl	In A und C fehlen die >. In GGA Angabe der Akzente entsprechend T. 35 und 40.
33	Kl	In A und C_1 fehlt *tre corde*.

37	Vl	A und C_1 haben *ces²* (statt *c²*) als 2. Viertel, was Grieg in C entsprechend T. 35 in Kl korrigierte.
83–90	Kl	A und C_1 haben 𝄻 unter allen arpeggierten Akkorden im angegebenen Bereich (vgl. Parallelstelle T. 283–290). GGA folgt C, das zweifellos die Angaben hat, zu denen sich Grieg bei der Korrektur entschloss.
83–90	Kl–s	In GGA > entsprechend T. 283–290. A und C sind beide inkonsequent. Die stringenteste Schreibweise hat SC.
93	Kl	In A und C_1 fehlt *una corda*.
93, 94, 97, 98	Vl	In A und C_1 fehlen Legatobögen für die letzten beiden Noten jedes Taktes, ergänzt in C. Dasselbe gilt für T. 293, 294, 297 und 298.
99	Kl	In A und C_1 fehlt *tre corde*.
101–102	Vl	A hat folgende Notierung, die Grieg vermutlich bei der Korrektur geändert hat:

113	Kl–s	In A fehlt die Metronomangabe.
132	Vl	In A keine Tenutostriche, ebenso T. 140, 164 und 172.
143–144	Vl	In A kein Phrasierungsbogen von d^1 nach *a*.
175–176	Vl	In A kein Phrasierungsbogen von d^2 nach a^1.
195	Kl	In A fehlt *sempre*.
200	Kl–s	A hat *a tempo*.
205	Kl	Linke Hand: > und ⟨ in GGA entsprechend T. 209 sowie Vl, die Kl kanonisch imitiert.
211	Kl	In A und C_1 fehlt 𝄻.
217	Vl	Wie oben T. 19.
221	Kl	In A und C_1 fehlt *una corda*.
221–234	Kl–s	C weicht gänzlich von A ab. Grieg hat die Stelle bei der Korrektur wesentlich geändert. Lesart A:

(Das Notenbeispiel war in GGA teilweise fehlerhaft wiedergegeben.)

223, 225	Kl	> in GGA entsprechend T. 23 und 25.
233	Kl	*tre corde* fehlt in A und C_1.
235–240	Vl	In A fehlen > für alle Doppelgriffe.
259–265	Kl	In GGA > über dem letzten Viertel in jedem Takt entsprechend T. 59–65 in C.
274	Kl	Rechte Hand: In A und C_1 leerer Takt.
275	Kl	In A fehlt **pp**.
283–290	Kl	A und C_1 haben 𝄻 unter den arpeggierten Akkorden im angegebenen Bereich (vgl. T. 83–90).
293	Kl	In A und C_1 fehlt *una corda*.
293, 294, 297, 298	Vl	Vgl. oben T. 93, 94, 97 und 98.
296	Vl	In C fehlt >.
299	Kl	In A und C_1 fehlt *tre corde*.
301–302	Vl	A hat folgende transponierte Parallele zu T. 101–102, die Grieg vermutlich bei der Korrektur von C änderte:

307–308	Vl	A hat nachstehende Lesart, die Grieg vermutlich bei der Korrektur änderte:

319	Kl–s	In A ohne Metronomangabe und ohne *a tempo*, in C mit Metronomangabe, jedoch ohne *a tempo*. SC hat *cantabile ed espressivo* sowie *a tempo*.
321	Kl–s	C hat *poco a poco sempre più* ***f*** erst in T. 322. In GGA zu T. 321 verlagert entsprechend A (dort ohne *sempre*).
333–334	Kl	A hat nachstehende Lesart, die Grieg vermutlich bei der Korrektur änderte:

341	Vl	A hat Folgendes:
349	Vl	A hat Folgendes:
362	Vl	In C fehlt *rubato*.
363, 365	Kl	In A fehlt der Akkord der rechten Hand.
367	Kl–s	In A keine Metronomangabe.
384, 385	Vl	In A fehlt jeweils die untere Note des Doppelgriffs auf Zählzeit 1.

*

b) Klavierpart

Der Klavierpart der vorliegenden Ausgabe weicht in einigen Fällen vom Notentext der GGA ab. Dies betrifft zum einen gelegentliche Notationsversehen und -ungenauigkeiten, die nun richtiggestellt bzw. präzisiert werden können, zum anderen einige Änderungen, die sich als Konsequenz aus der Übernahme der Lesart SC (Violinpart) in die Partitur neu ergeben. Im Einzelnen handelt es sich um folgende Klavierpart-Abweichungen von GGA:

I. Satz:

Takt / Instrument / Kommentar

44	Kl	⎯⎯ eingefügt entsprechend T. 305.
79, 108	Kl	In C/GGA *pp*; zu *ppp* geändert entsprechend Vl/SC (vgl. T. 340, 369).
95	Kl	𝒫ℯ𝒹. eingefügt entsprechend Kontext.
141	Kl	*dim.* eingefügt entsprechend Vl/SC, T. 140/141 (Imitation).
145, 163, 400	Kl	In C/GGA *pp*; zu *ppp* geändert entsprechend Vl/SC.
169	Kl	In C/GGA *poco cresc.* erst ab T. 170 (analog Vl); verlagert entsprechend Kl., T. 151.
172	Kl	In C/GGA *più cresc.* bereits ab Taktbeginn; verlagert entsprechend T. 154.
178	Kl	*ff* eingefügt entsprechend Vl/SC.
238	Kl	In C/GGA *cresc.* erst ab Mitte T. 239; verlagert entsprechend Vl/SC.
283	Kl	Rechte Hand, Unterstimme: Legatobogen für *des-c* ergänzt entsprechend T. 22.
314	Kl	Staccatopunkte ergänzt entsprechend T. 53 und Kontext.
340, 369	Kl	In C/GGA *pp*; zu *ppp* geändert entsprechend Vl/SC (vgl. T. 79, 108).
375	Kl	*pp tranquillo* eingefügt entsprechend T. 114.

II. Satz:

Takt / Instrument / Kommentar

171, 175, 183	Kl	Rechte Hand: jeweils Staccatopunkt für ♪-Note eingefügt entsprechend Kontext (vgl. T. 107, 111, 155, 163).
199	Kl	Linke Hand: Akzent > eingefügt entsprechend T. 195.
206–208	Kl	In C/GGA ⎯⎯ in T. 206–207; verlagert zu T. 207–208 entsprechend Vl/SC (dort leicht ungenau).

III. Satz:

Takt / Instrument / Kommentar

17	Kl	In C/GGA *cresc.* bereits in T. 16, letzte Triole; nach T. 17 verlagert entsprechend T. 215.
25, 29, 35	Kl	In C/GGA uneinheitliche Länge der ⎯⎯; vereinheitlicht entsprechend T. 39 und Vl/SC.
39	Kl	Rechte Hand: Staccatopunkt für letzte Note eingefügt entsprechend Kontext.
45/46, 49/50	Kl	In C/GGA jeweils über den Taktstrich reichende ⎯⎯ (Zählzeit 4–2); Gabel getilgt entsprechend Vl/SC.

101–110	Kl	In C/GGA (zurückgehend auf Griegs ungenaue Notation in A) inkonsequente Setzung der Staccatopunkte; offensichtlich fehlende Punkte eingefügt (vgl. auch die erweiterte Parallelstelle, T. 301–316).
205–239	Kl	In C/GGA uneinheitliche Länge der ⎯⎯ im angegebenen Bereich; vereinheitlicht entsprechend Vl/SC (vgl. auch oben, T. 25, 29, 35).
221	Kl	*pp* eingefügt entsprechend Vl.
235	Kl	Rechte Hand: Akzent für 1. Note eingefügt entsprechend T. 229.
245/246, 249/250	Kl	In C/GGA in T. 245/246 (Zählzeit 4–2) und T. 249/250 (Zählzeit 3–2) ⎯⎯; getilgt entsprechend Vl/SC.
253	Kl	Staccatopunkt ergänzt entsprechend T. 257 und Kontext.
303, 305	Kl	*fz* eingefügt entsprechend T. 309.
304, 311	Kl	Rechte Hand, Zählzeit 4: Staccatopunkt ergänzt entsprechend Kontext (vgl. auch oben T. 101–110).

*

c) Violinpart

Wie oben ausgeführt und begründet, übernimmt die vorliegende Ausgabe – abweichend von GGA – die Lesart der separaten Solostimme (SC) auch in die Partitur. Diese von Grieg zwar intendierte, seit der Erstausgabe (1887) aber nur in der separaten Solostimme, nicht in der Partitur, überlieferte Lesart zeichnet sich durch kleinere, jedoch wichtige Nuancen mit spielpraktischer Relevanz aus (Akzente, Dynamik, Bögen etc.). Änderungen, die sich durch die Aufwertung und Übernahme von SC gegenüber GGA ergeben, sind in den folgenden Einzelanmerkungen *nicht* nachgewiesen; erwähnt werden vielmehr alle Stellen, an denen der Violinpart der vorliegende Ausgabe von Quelle SC abweicht bzw. diese korrigiert. Einige Sonderzeichen (wie Fingersatzangaben, *sul G* etc.), die nur in der separaten Stimme erscheinen, sowie minimale Justierungen bleiben unerwähnt.

I. Satz:

Takt / Instrument / Kommentar

11–14	Vl	Zählzeit 4: In SC jeweils ohne Akzent für ♪-Note; ergänzt entsprechend T. 272–275.
31	Vl	In SC *cresc.* erst ab Taktmitte; verlagert entsprechend Kl.
87	Vl	In SC nur *cresc.*; *poco a poco* ergänzt entsprechend Kl.
91, 352	Vl	In SC jeweils ohne *sempre cresc.*; eingefügt entsprechend Kl.
119	Vl	In SC ohne ⎯⎯; eingefügt entsprechend T. 116.
121	Vl	In SC ohne Akzent auf der 2. Note; eingefügt entsprechend T. 382.
136–137	Vl	In SC jeweils ohne ⎯⎯; eingefügt entsprechend Kontext.
160–162, 178–180	Vl	In SC jeweils mit zusätzlichem, über drei volle Takte reichendem Legatobogen.

206	Vl	In SC ohne *tranquillo*; eingefügt entsprechend Kl.
212	Vl	In SC mit Akzent, vermutlich irrtümlich gesetzt; getilgt entsprechend T. 218.
284	Vl	In SC ohne *cantabile*; eingefügt entsprechend T. 23.
315	Vl	In SC *p*; zu *pp* geändert entsprechend T. 54 und Kl, T. 316.
378	Vl	In SC ohne *cresc. poco a poco*; eingefügt entsprechend Kl und T. 117.
385	Vl	In SC *dim.* erst ab ♪-Note a^1; verlagert entsprechend T. 124.
410–411	Vl	In SC ohne ⟨; eingefügt entsprechend Kl.
414	Vl	In SC ohne Tenutostriche; eingefügt entsprechend B.
415, 418	Vl	In SC ohne *ff*; eingefügt entsprechend Kl.
440	Vl	In SC 2. Note mit Akzent; getilgt entsprechend B.

II. Satz:

Takt / Instrument / Kommentar

143	Vl	In SC ohne ⟩ ; eingefügt entsprechend T. 139.
147–148	Vl	In SC ⟩ nur bis Ende T. 147; verlängert entsprechend Kl.
183 ff.	Vl	In SC nur *ritardando*, Beginn erst in T. 185; nach T. 183 verlagert und zu *ritardando poco a poco* erweitert entsprechend Kl.
217/218	Vl	In SC nur *cresc.*; zu *cresc. ed appassionato* erweitert entsprechend Kl.
236	Vl	In SC *ritardando* (T. 235–236); zu *poco rit.* (T. 236) geändert entsprechend Kl.
245	Vl	In SC *ritardando* (T. 246–248); zu *poco rit.* geändert entsprechend Kl (T. 246), nach T. 245 verlagert entsprechend T. 81.
246	Vl	In SC 1. Note mit Akzent; getilgt entsprechend T. 82.
256–260	Vl	In SC *poco a poco ritardando sempre* (T. 255–263); zu *poco a poco sempre più ritardando* (T. 256–260) geändert entsprechend Kl.

III. Satz:

Takt / Instrument / Kommentar

27, 31	Vl	In SC ⟨ jeweils ab Zählzeit 2; geändert entsprechend T. 37 und 41 (dort leicht ungenau).
37	Vl	In SC 1. Note ohne Akzent; eingefügt entsprechend T. 31.
61, 65	Vl	In SC jeweils 1. Note ohne Akzent; eingefügt entsprechend T. 261 und 265.
67	Vl	In SC nur *dim.*; zu *dim e tranquillo* erweitert entsprechend T. 267.
95	Vl	In SC 1. Note ohne Akzent; ergänzt entsprechend T. 5 und 295.
147–148	Vl	In SC ⟨ nur in T. 148; Beginn verlagert nach T. 147 entsprechend SC, T. 115–116, und B, T. 147–148.
168	Vl	In SC ohne ⟩ ; eingefügt entsprechend T. 136.
200	Vl	In SC *pp*; zu *p* geändert entsprechend T. 2.
203	Vl	In SC 1. Note ohne Akzent; eingefügt entsprechend T. 5.
228, 232, 238, 242	Vl	In SC jeweils ♩-Note ohne Akzent; eingefügt entsprechend T. 38 und 42.
231	Vl	In SC letzte Note ohne Staccatopunkt; eingefügt entsprechend T. 31.
243	Vl	In SC ohne *animato*; eingefügt entsprechend T. 43.
261, 265	Vl	In SC ohne ⟨; eingefügt entsprechend Kontext.
275–276	Vl	In SC anstelle ⟨ ⟩ nur ⟨ in T. 276; geändert entsprechend T. 75–76.
288	Vl	In SC *cresc.* bereits in T. 287, 2. Takthälfte; nach T. 288 verlagert entsprechend Kl.
296	Vl	In SC ohne Akzent; eingefügt entsprechend T. 96.
304, 306	Vl	In SC jeweils ♩-Note ohne Akzent; eingefügt entsprechend T. 104 und 106.
318	Vl	In SC Akkord ohne Akzent; eingefügt entsprechend Kontext.
325	Vl	In SC ohne Akzent; eingefügt entsprechend T. 357 und Kontext.
342	Vl	In SC ohne ⟩ ; eingefügt entsprechend T. 136.
352	Vl	In SC ohne ⟨; eingefügt entsprechend Kl und T. 354.

Editorial Commentary

The variant readings reproduced below are mostly taken from the complete edition of Edvard Grieg's works, *Edvard-Grieg-Gesamtausgabe* (GGA), edited by the Edvard Grieg Committee, Oslo, where they appear in volume 8, *Sonatas for Violin and Piano* (and other chamber-music works), edited by Finn Benestad (Frankfurt am Main, 1979). The text has been editorially revised and expanded for the present edition.

Since the publication in 1979 of GGA, volume 8, much new research material on Grieg and his music has come to light. Around 3,000 published letters by Grieg, extensive biographical publications, analytical books and articles, diaries and account books have given new insight into Grieg's life and oeuvre. Biographical information related to the C-minor sonata is documented in footnotes in the preface of the present edition.

The discussion of the *Source Material* has been modified to incorporate new information, particularly concerning a stronger differentiation of source C, which was first made possible through the investigation of the C. F. Peters historical printing records (*Auflagebücher*). Thereby source S, the separate solo part of C, could be accorded a greater editorial relevance than it had been given in the GGA score.

The extended source material is dealt with below in the three-part list of *Variants*.

*

The *Sonata for Violin and Piano* in C minor No. 3 Op. 45 is Edvard Grieg's last violin sonata. It was composed at "Troldhaugen" near Bergen in the autumn and winter of 1886. The first edition was published in November 1887 by C. F. Peters, Leipzig. The sonata is dedicated to German portrait painter Franz von Lenbach (1836–1904).

The first performance took place at the Neues Gewandhaus in Leipzig on 10 December 1887, played by the Russian violinist Adolph Brodsky (1851–1929) and the composer.

The Source Material

A:

Autograph of the piano score in Bergen Offentlige Bibliotek (Bergen Public Library); without separate violin part.

The manuscript (MS) consists of 22 loose sheets with four full systems (violin part & piano part) on each page. The paper is marked *C. A. Klemm. C. Nº 7*. The two sides of the title page are not numbered, and p. [25a] is blank. There are also two blank and unnumbered pages after p. 39. The format is 35,6 x 26,2 cm.

The title page is inscribed in ink as follows: *F. v. Lenbach / gewidmet. / Sonate / für Pianoforte und Violine / (Nº 3, C moll) / von / Edvard Grieg. / op. 45*. At the top of the title page there is an addition in blue colour, not in Grieg's handwriting: *Bis 19/11* and *Nr. 54347*. At the bottom of the title page the following is added in pencil, not in Grieg's handwriting: *Fortsetzung zu 7178 / Violinstimme folgt / 15/11.87*. Similar additions are found on p. 1: *Buchstaben einziehen?* On p. 18: *12/11/87*, and on p. 39: *15/11/87 / Kühn und schwungvoll, hab's gern so*. MS is clearly legible.

Division of the movements:

pp. 1–18: I. *Allegro molto ed appassionato.* M. M. $\downarrow$ = 116

pp. 19–25: II. *Allegretto espressivo alla Romanza.* [no metronome indication]

pp. 26–39: III. *Allegro animato.* $\downarrow$ = [no metronome figure given]

Corrections:

Additions have been made throughout the autograph in red colour or with pencil. Most of these refer to pedalling.

Provenance:

The autograph was the printer's copy for the first edition. Through several decades it was preserved in a private collection in London. It is not known how and when it was transferred to this collection. The Bergen Public Library – with financial support from Kavlis almennyttige fond and G. C. Rieber & Co., Bergen – bought the autograph in 2005 from Musikantiquariat Dr. Ulrich Drüner, Stuttgart, for £40,000.[1]

B:

The Royal Northern College of Music, Manchester (formerly the Royal Manchester College of Music) has a separate violin part of the C-minor sonata in Grieg's autograph. Since December 1897 the autograph was owned by the Russian violin virtuoso Adolph Brodsky, who subsequently willed it to the Royal Manchester College of Music.

The title page has the following inscription in Grieg's handwriting: *Ich bezeuge hiermit, dass: / Diese Stimme ist nicht etwa von / Brodsky geschrieben, sondern von seinem / Freund und kolossaler* [!] *Verehrer / Edvard Grieg / Manchester 19/12/97 / Violino.*

In spite of the dated dedication in Grieg's own hand, it is impossible to say when B was written, although the possibility of this manuscript serving as printer's copy for the first edition (1887) can be ruled out, since it contains no engraver's marks. B most likely must be seen in direct connection with the handwritten MS of the solo part that Grieg brought with him from Troldhaugen to Leipzig to scrutinize it in November 1887 with his countryman, violinist Johan Halvorsen, who by that time studied violin with Adolph Brodsky in Leipzig (see Preface). After their co-operation, Grieg delivered B – including a large number of changes made by Halvorsen and sanctioned by the composer – to the publisher (*Violinstimme folgt*, see Source C). Thus, most likely, B is a fair copy of the (missing) printer's copy of SC.

We do not know when and on which occasion Grieg gave the manuscript to Adolph Brodsky, whether as a token of gratitude for his brilliant premiere performance of the sonata (10 December 1887) or as a generous gesture when visiting the Brodsky familiy in Manchester ten years later. Be that as it may, on 19 December 1897 Grieg wrote the authentication reproduced above on the title page of the MS.

C:

The *First Edition* was published in November 1887 by C. F. Peters, Leipzig, pl. no. 7178 (Edition Peters No. 2414), 45 + 11 pages in Peters edition format.

The title page has the following text: *Franz von Lenbach / gewidmet. / Sonate / (C moll) / für Pianoforte und Violine / von / EDVARD GRIEG / Op. 45. / Eigenthum des Verlegers. / LEIPZIG / C. F. PETERS. / F. Baumgarten, del.*

The following printed copies have served as source material for the present edition:

1st printing (first edition),[2] November 1887 (C_1). A copy preserved at Nasjonalbiblioteket (The National Library) Oslo has the following dedication: *Til min kjære Ven og Landsmand Johan Halvorsen fra Din heng. Edvard Grieg. Leipzig Dcbr 87.* ("To my dear friend and compatriot Johan Halvorsen from Your devoted Edvard Grieg. Leipzig Dcbr 87.")

2nd printing, December 1887 (C). A copy preserved at Bergen Offentlige Bibliotek (The Bergen Public Library) has the following dedication from Grieg to his wife Nina Grieg: *Med kjærlig Julehilsen fra Din Edv.* ("With loving Christmas greetings from Your Edv.").

The first edition, which was issued in late November 1887 (500 copies) was an immediate success. Already in December of the same year, C. F. Peters published another impression (1,000 copies). A reprint of this was published in May 1888 (1,000 copies), and during the following years the sonata appeared in a continuous series of reprints. By 1906 it had reached the incredible number of 29,000 copies, all of which bear the original plate number (7178). C. F. Peters published no new edition during Grieg's lifetime.

Compared to the first printing (C_1), the second printing (C) contains a large number of minor corrections (for example changes of dynamics, bowing and pedalling), which must have been initiated or sanctioned by the composer. To a somewhat lesser degree than the score, the separate solo part (S), in the transition from SC_1 to SC, also received a few corrections. Thus, in the third movement, b. 37, the second note was changed from cb^2 to c^2, and some of the fingerings in the first movement were adjusted. However, in all three movements of SC_1/SC there are numerous deviations from the violin part of the score (Vl), particularly regarding dynamics. This is due to the fact that the violin part of source A was replaced by the missing separate violin part prepared to become the engraver's copy for SC_1/SC (cf. Source B). The final MS to be printed was SC_1, which – apart from the above-mentioned small changes in SC – remained unchanged in all subsequent impressions. A transfer of the SC version into the violin part in the score (Vl) never occurred, and since there were no wrong notes in Vl, the publisher apparently saw no need for changes. Grieg himself apparently did not persistently urge the publishing company to make any changes in the score. It is regrettable that neither the engraver's copy of the separate solo part nor any proofs of the sonata are preserved. Moreover, no available related correspondence between Grieg and Max Abraham refers to the printing process, due to the fact that Grieg lived in Leipzig during this time and had access to C. F. Peters whenever he wanted.

Source C gives the musical text in a state that was sanctioned by the composer. That is the reason why P–s in C was the main source of the GGA edition of the C-minor sonata. The present edition is based on GGA. However, as for the separate violin part, which is based on Grieg's and Halvorsen's final version of SC, this part is generally given editorial priority, particularly regarding dynamics. SC, in comparison to Vl in C, is more complete and refined. Thus SC, though containing some engraver's errors and inaccuracies, best represents the final version of the work as intended by Grieg.

*

Abbreviations used in the list of variants:

GGA: *Grieg-Gesamtausgabe*, volume 8, which also forms the basis of the present edition.

A, B, C and C_1: the sources mentioned above.

P–s: both parts (violin and piano) in the piano score.

P: the piano part in the piano score.

Vl: the violin part in the piano score.

S: the separate solo part of C (= SC) or C_1 (= SC_1).

Where source differences occur between SC and Vl, the present edition – unlike GGA – gives priority to SC, transferring most of this version to Vl in the score. Most likely, the new edition thereby – for the first time in a Peters edition – comes close to Grieg's intention regarding the violin part of the score. This transfer can be done without detailed documentation in the list of variants, since the new printed version of Vl is identical with SC, which had been legitimized by Grieg. Furthermore, the previous violin part can always be seen in the GGA edition. However, the list of variants at the end of the Editorial Commentary (section c) contains a documentation of the cases in which the present edition of Vl deviates from SC. A change in Vl that may cause a change in P will be commented upon in section b.

Since SC_1 and SC are nearly identical, the variants generally refer only to SC.

SC_1, SC and B are furnished with fingerings, especially in the first movement. In B most of them, for some unknown reason, are bracketed. The fingerings, most likely prepared by Halvorsen and sanctioned by Grieg, are retained in the separate solo part of the present edition, with a few minor adjustments.

[1] Information kindly given by Siren Steen, head of the Grieg Collection (Griegsamligen), Bergen Offentlige Bibliotek. The editor wishes to express his sincere gratitude to her for her extensive support in connection with the present edition.

[2] The various stages from the first printing through a number of successive impressions, as well as the differences between them, have kindly been confirmed by Øyvind Norheim, one of the editors of the *Grieg-Werkverzeichnis* (see Preface, footnote 13), which was published in 2008, as the conclusion to GGA.

Variants

Full score (a) · Piano part (b) · Violin part (c)

a) Full score

The following detailed comments are taken from GGA, volume 8, with minor revisions and some additional variants (concerning sources A and C₁). Comments referring to discrepancies between the full score and SC (violin part) have been omitted, since the full score of the present edition – unlike that of GGA – directly follows the text of SC.

1st movement: *Allegro molto ed appassionato* M.M. ♩. = 116.

bar / instrument / comment

5	Vl	C lacks natural to the second note.
67–78	P	A has an incomplete pedal notation. GGA is in accordance with C. Grieg no doubt made additions and corrections in the proofs.
79	P	A and C₁ lack *una corda*.
87	P	A and C₁ lack *tre corde*. See also b. 348.
103–107	P	A has misplaced pedal indications which must have been corrected by Grieg in the proofs.
114	P	A lacks *tre corde*.
114–163	P	All pedal markings (𝄐. and *) missing in A and C₁. Cf. bb. 67–78.
116–117	P–s	C has *molto cresc. poco a poco*; *molto* is unwarranted here and belongs in b. 121. Cf. b. 378.
129–143	P-s	A has ⟨ ⟩ in b. 130. For Vl A lacks all hairpins in this section.
135–136	P–s	A and C have *cresc. molto e ritard.* GGA uses *cresc. molto e poco ritard.*, as do B and SC.
178, 184	P	𝄐. missing in A and C₁.
206	Vl	*tranquillo* has been omitted in B.
249	Vl	A and C₁ have only the top notes; corrected in C.
261	Vl	C lacks accents.
284	Vl	A lacks natural to the second note.
325	Vl	Grace notes missing in A and C₁.
328–339	P	A lacks pedal markings.
340	P	A and C₁ lack *una corda*.
348	P	A lacks 𝄐. and *tre corde*.
377	P	C has an unwarranted ⟨.
382–385	P–s	*molto* in b. 385 in C is wrong; *molto* belongs with *cresc.* in bb. 382/383 as in SC.
386	Vl	The slur is omitted in C.
390–398	P–s	The dynamic markings in C are not identical with those in A and B. GGA follows A and B.
418–423	Vl	In C the first note of each bar lacks >.
430	P–s	A lacks metronome figure.
433	Vl	C lacks > on the first note.
433	P	Right hand: A and C₁ have *d-d♭* in the lower notes; in C corrected to *d♭-d♭*.

2nd movement: *Allegretto espressivo alla Romanza* M.M. ♩ = 72.

bar / instrument / comment

1	P–s	A lacks metronome indication.
14	P	A has *f*. GGA follows C.

25	P	A and C₁ have an arpeggio line for both systems. GGA follows C which seems to be most in accordance with the parallel passage in b. 27 and was most likely corrected in the proofs by Grieg.
29, 33, 37	P	A has an arpeggio line only for the left hand (in C for both hands). It was most likely corrected in the proofs by Grieg.
60–61	Vl	C has *dolcissimo*. GGA uses *dolce* as does SC.
73	Vl	C lacks *p*.
78	Vl	*più agitato* is omitted in C.
86	P–s	*rit.* is omitted in C.
89	P–s	A lacks metronome indication.
89	Vl	C has *ma marcato* instead of *ma poco marcato*.
97, 101	Vl	A has portato (-) instead of accents (>).
105	Vl	C has *poco marcato* instead of *p ma poco marcato*.
105	P–s	*a tempo* is omitted in A and in both parts of C.
128	Kl	C lacks ⟩.
139	P	The sources show a general disagreement concerning dynamic markings. GGA has *ffz* by analogy with b. 143 in C. It is a common indication with Grieg.
146–147	P	C has a misplaced ⟩. In GGA it is moved to bb. 147–148 in accordance with Vl.
156	Vl	C lacks ⟨.
160	P	C lacks ⟩.
164	Vl	C lacks ⟨. Cf. b. 156.
164	P	Left hand: A and C₁ lack the tied ♩ *b* from b. 163.
175	P	A lacks > on the first note.
180	P	A and C₁ have only ♩ *a-c¹* in the upper part of the lower system, played here by the right hand.
194	Vl	C lacks *espressivo*.
225	Vl	C lacks *dolce*.
265	Vl	C lacks *ppp*.

3rd movement: *Allegro animato* ♩ = 104

bar / instrument / comment

1	P–s	A lacks metronome figure.
6	P	A lacks staccato under *g¹* in the lower system.
19, 217	Vl	A has  [pizz. notation], which was certainly corrected in the proofs by Grieg.
22	P	*una corda* missing in A and C₁.
25, 30	P	Accent (>) is missing in A and C. GGA has > by analogy with bb. 35 and 40.
33	P	*tre corde* missing in A and C₁.
37	Vl	In A and C₁ the second note is *c♭²* (instead of *c²*). This was corrected by Grieg in C and is also in accordance with P in b. 35.

83–90	P	A and C₁ have 𝒫ℯ𝒹. under each arpeggio chord. GGA follows C which undoubtedly represents Grieg's decisions during proof reading. The same applies to bb. 283–290.
83–90	P–s	GGA has > by analogy with bb. 283–290. SC is more consistent than A and C.
93	P	A and C₁ lack *una corda*.
93, 94, 97, 98	Vl	A and C₁ have no slur between the last two notes of each bar. The slurs have been inserted in C.
99	P	*tre corde* missing in A and C₁.
101–102	Vl	A has the following notation which must have been changed by Grieg in the proofs:

113	P–s	A lacks metronome indication.
132	Vl	A lacks portato marking. The same applies to bb. 140, 164 and 172.
143–144	Vl	A lacks the slur from d^1 to a.
175–176	Vl	A lacks the slur from d^2 to a^1.
195	P	A lacks *sempre*.
200	P–s	A has *a tempo*.
205	P	Left hand: GGA has > and ⟵ to agree with b. 209. It is also in canonic imitation with Vl.
211	P	𝒫ℯ𝒹. missing in A and C₁.
217	Vl	As b. 19.
221	Kl	A and C₁ lack *una corda*.
221–234	P–s	C is very different from A, so Grieg must have made important proof corrections. A has:

(In GGA this music example was reproduced with some errors.)

223, 225	P	GGA has > to agree with bb. 23 and 25.
233	P	*tre corde* missing in A and C₁.

235–240	Vl	A lacks > on all the double stops.
259–265	P	GGA has > on the last crotchet of each bar in accordance with bb. 59–65 in C.
274	P	Right hand: in A and C₁ the whole bar is empty.
275	P–s	A lacks ***pp***.
283–290	P	A and C₁ have 𝒫ℯ𝒹. under each arpeggio chord within this section. Similarly in bb. 83–90.
293	P	*una corda* missing in A and C₁.
293, 294, 297, 298	Vl	Cf. bb. 93, 94, 97 and 98.
296	Vl	C lacks >.
299	P	A and C₁ lack *tre corde*.
301–302	Vl	A has a transposed parallel to bb. 101–102. Grieg no doubt made a proof correction for C. A has:

307–308	Vl	A has the following notation which must have been corrected in the proofs by Grieg:

319	P–s	A lacks metronome indication and *a tempo*. C has metronome indication but no *a tempo*. SC has *cantabile ed espressivo* as well as metronome indication and *a tempo*.
321	P–s	C has *poco a poco sempre più **f*** in b. 322. In GGA this marking is brought forward to b. 321 in accordance with A (in which *sempre* is omitted).
333–334	P	A has the following notation which must have been corrected by Grieg in the proofs:

341	Vl	A has the following notation: 
349	Vl	A has the following notation:
362	Vl	C lacks *rubato*.
363, 365	P	A lacks the right-hand chord.
367	P–s	A lacks metronome markings.
384, 385	Vl	A lacks the lower note of the double stop on first beat of each bar.

*

b) Piano part

The piano part of the present edition differs from GGA in some places. These include occasional corrections and clarifications of notational errors and inaccuracies, as well as changes necessitated by adopting the text of SC (violin part) in the full score. Specifically, the piano part deviates from GGA in the following instances:

1st movement:

bar / instrument / comment

44	P	$<$ inserted in accordance with b. 305.
79, 108	P	C/GGA have *pp*; changed to *ppp* in accordance with Vl/SC (cf. bb. 340, 369).
95	P	℘ℯ𝒹. inserted in accordance with musical context.
141	P	*dim.* inserted in accordance with Vl/SC, bb. 140/141 (imitation).
145, 163, 400	P	C/GGA have *pp*; changed to *pp* in accordance with Vl/SC.
169	P	C/GGA have *poco cresc.* in b. 170 (as does Vl in C); moved in accordance with P, b. 151.
172	P	C/GGA have *più cresc.* from beginning of the bar; moved in accordance with b. 154.
178	P	*ff* inserted in accordance with Vl/SC.
238	P	C/GGA have *cresc.* from middle of b. 239; moved in accordance with Vl/SC.
283	P	Right hand, lower voice: slur for *db-c* inserted in accordance with b. 22.
314	P	Staccato dots inserted in accordance with b. 53 and musical context.
340, 369	P	C/GGA have *pp*; changed to *ppp* in accordance with Vl/SC (cf. b. 79, 108).
375	P	*pp tranquillo* inserted in accordance with b. 114.

2nd movement:

bar / instrument / comment

171, 175, 183	P	Right hand: staccato dot for each ♪ inserted in accordance with musical context (cf. bb. 107, 111, 155, 163).
199	P	Left hand: accent > inserted in accordance with b. 195.
206–208	P	C/GGA have $>$ in bb. 206–207; moved to bb. 207–208 in accordance with Vl/SC (there somewhat inaccurately positioned).

3rd movement:

bar / instrument / comment

17	P	In C/GGA *cresc.* already from last triplet in b. 16; moved to b. 17 in accordance b. 215.
25, 29, 35	P	C/GGA have inconsistent length of $<$; standardized in accordance with b. 39 and Vl/SC.
39	P	Right hand: staccato dot for last note inserted in accordance with musical context.
45/46, 49/50	P	C/GGA have $<$ across the bar-line (beats 4–2); eliminated in accordance with Vl/SC.

101–110	P	C/GGA (due to Grieg's inaccurate notation in A) lack a great number of staccato dots, which have been inserted (cf. the extended parallel passage in bb. 301–316).
205–239	P	C/GGA have inconsistent length of $<$ in this section; standardized in accordance with Vl/SC (cf. bb. 25, 29, 35).
221	P	*pp* inserted in accordance with Vl in C.
235	P	Right hand: accent for first note inserted in accordance with b. 229.
245/246, 249/250	P	C/GGA have $<$ in bb. 245/246 (beats 4–2) and bb. 249/250 (beats 3–2); deleted in accordance with Vl/SC.
253	P	Staccato dot inserted in accordance with b. 257 and musical context.
303, 305	P	*fz* inserted in accordance with b. 309.
304, 311	P	Right hand, beat 4: staccato dot inserted in accordance with musical context (cf. bb. 101–110).

*

c) Violin part

As explained above, the present edition – unlike GGA – adopts the text of the separate solo part (SC) also in the full score. This version represents Grieg's intentions but was not incorporated in the first edition of 1887 or any of the subsequent editions, except in the solo part. It is characterised by small but important differences that carry implications for performance (accents, dynamics, slurs etc.). Changes to the text of GGA which result from reassessing and adopting source SC are *not* listed in the following comments; instead they refer to all instances where the present edition differs from or corrects the text of SC. Some specific indications which only appear in the separate solo part (such as fingerings, *sul G* etc.), as well as minimal adjustments, have not been noted.

1st movement:

bar / instrument / comment

11–14	Vl	Fourth beat: SC lacks accent for each ♪; inserted in accordance with bb. 272–275.
31	Vl	SC postpones *cresc.* to middle of this bar; moved in accordance with P.
87	Vl	SC has only *cresc.*; *poco a poco* added in accordance with P.
91, 352	Vl	SC lacks *sempre cresc.*; inserted in accordance with P.
119	Vl	SC lacks $>$; inserted in accordance with b. 116.
121	Vl	SC lacks accent for the second note; inserted in accordance with b. 382.
136–137	Vl	SC lacks $>$; inserted in both bars in accordance with musical context.
160–162, 178–180	Vl	SC has an additional slur from b. 160 to b. 162 and from b. 178 to b. 180.
206	Vl	SC lacks *tranquillo*; inserted in accordance with P.
212	Vl	SC has accent, presumably wrongly engraved; deleted in accordance with b. 218.
284	Vl	SC lacks *cantabile*; inserted in accordance with b. 23.

315	Vl	SC has *p*; changed to **pp** in accordance with b. 54 and P, b. 316.
378	Vl	SC lacks *cresc. poco a poco*; inserted in accordance with P and b. 117.
385	Vl	SC moves *dim.* to ♪*a*¹ in accordance with b. 124.
410–411	Vl	SC lacks ⟨; inserted in accordance with P.
414	Vl	SC lacks tenuto dashes; inserted in accordance with B.
415, 418	Vl	SC lacks **ff**; inserted in accordance with P.
440	Vl	SC has accent on the second note; deleted in accordance with B.

2nd movement:

bar / instrument / comment

143	Vl	SC lacks ⟩; inserted in accordance with b. 139.
147–148	Vl	In SC ⟩ only until the end of b. 147; extended in accordance with P.
183 ff.	Vl	SC has *ritardando* from b. 185; moved to b. 183 and completed to *ritardando poco a poco* in accordance with P.
217/218	Vl	SC has only *cresc.*; changed to *cresc. ed appassionato* in accordance with P.
236	Vl	SC has *ritardando* (bb. 235–236); changed to *poco rit.* (b. 236) in accordance with P.
245	Vl	SC has *ritardando* (bb. 246–248); changed to *poco rit.* in accordance with P (b. 246), and moved to b. 245 in accordance with b. 81.
246	Vl	SC has accent on the first note; deleted in accordance with b. 82.
256–260	Vl	SC has *poco a poco ritardando sempre* (bb. 255–263); changed to *poco a poco sempre più ritardando* (bb. 256–260) in accordance with P.

3rd movement:

bar / instrument / comment

| 27, 31 | Vl | SC has ⟨ from second beat; changed in accordance with b. 37 and 41 (there somewhat inaccurately positioned). |
| 37 | Vl | SC lacks accent on the first note; inserted in accordance with b. 31. |

61, 65	Vl	SC lacks accent on the first note in both bars; inserted in accordance with b. 261 and b. 265.
67	Vl	SC has only *dim.*; changed to *dim e tranquillo* in accordance with b. 267.
95	Vl	SC lacks accent on first note; inserted in accordance with b. 5 and b. 295.
147–148	Vl	In SC ⟨ only in b. 148; start moved to b. 147 in accordance with SC, bb. 115–116, and B, bb. 147–148.
168	Vl	SC lacks ⟩; inserted in accordance with b. 136.
200	Vl	SC has **pp**; changed to **p** in accordance with b. 2.
203	Vl	SC lacks accent on first note; inserted in accordance with b. 5.
228, 232, 238, 242	Vl	SC lacks accent on ♩; inserted in accordance with b. 38 and b. 42.
231	Vl	SC lacks staccato dot on the last note; inserted in accordance with b. 31.
243	Vl	SC lacks *animato*; inserted in accordance with b. 43.
261, 265	Vl	SC lacks ⟨; inserted in accordance with musical context.
275–276	Vl	SC has only ⟨ instead of ⟨ ⟩ in b. 276; changed in accordance with bb. 75–76.
288	Vl	SC postpones *cresc.* to b. 287 (third beat); moved to b. 288 in accordance with P.
296	Vl	SC lacks accent; inserted in accordance with b. 96.
304, 306	Vl	SC lacks accent on ♩; inserted in accordance with b. 104 and b. 106.
318	Vl	SC lacks accent on the chord (third beat); inserted in accordance with musical context.
325	Vl	SC lacks accent; inserted in accordance with b. 357 and musical context.
342	Vl	SC lacks ⟩; inserted in accordance with b. 136.
352	Vl	SC lacks ⟨; inserted in accordance with P and b. 354.

Inhalt / Contents

Aufführungsdauer / Duration: ca. 25 Min.